Eleven Plus
Secondary School Selection

Mathematics
10 Practice Papers

Standard <u>and</u> multiple choice
Dual Format

© Internet Primary School 2004

Introduction

This book contains 10 shorter 11+/12+ maths papers.

We have covered many different types of question that we know may appear on the "real" test. You should remember that different areas may have slightly differing exams. There may also be a difference in the time allowed to complete the test.

The IPS 11+ Mathematics tests have been designed to be completed in approximately 35 minutes. Don't panic if you don't achieve this straight away. You will be able to see where your strengths and weaknesses lie and where you might need to concentrate your practice. All you can really do is work as fast as you can without making silly mistakes. If you rush, your work will be affected by little mistakes. You can use these papers for timed practice or just as revision exercises. The choice is up to you.

This book of papers comes in <u>DUAL FORMAT</u>. This means that use it in either standard format and write the answers directly onto the question paper, or multiple choice format, where answers are selected from a list on the multiple choice answer sheet. These answer sheets can be removed from the back of the book.

Make sure that you read the questions VERY carefully. Don't assume that just because a question _looks_ like one you have had before it is exactly the same type.

Good luck!

IPS 11+ Team 2004

Time started : 10.15   H/W 11/07/15

11+ Mathematics - Paper 1.

You have 35 minutes to complete this paper.

Q 1. Which of the following sum has the greatest value?   Circle the appropriate letter.

20   70   80   60   45

| 0.2 x 100 | ⅛ of 320 | 30% of 240 | 40 x 1.5 | ¼ of 180 |
| A | B | C | D | E |

(C circled)

[1]

Q 2. Which of these nets <u>will</u> fold to form a cube? Circle the appropriate letter or letters.

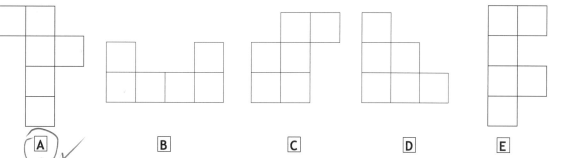

A   B   C   D   E

(A circled)

[1]

Q 3. What is the value of 2 cubed (2^3) ? Circle the appropriate letter.

2   6   16   10   8

A   B   C   D   E

(E circled)

[1]

Q 4. Find the missing number so that the equation balances.

47

$$29 + (6 \times 3) = 7 \times 5 + \underline{12}$$

[1]

Q 5.

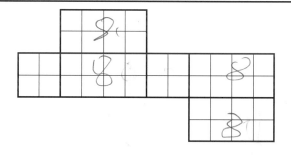

Look at the net to the left.

When folded it makes a box.

If the side of each small square is 1 cm,
what will be the total surface area of the box?   40 cm²

[1]

Q 6. Springfield Rovers played the Uptown Rangers in a football match.
The match kicked off at 2.45 p.m. They played 40 minutes each half,
and had a half-time break of 15 minutes.

At what time did the match end?

4.20 p.m.

[1]

6 / 6

HIW

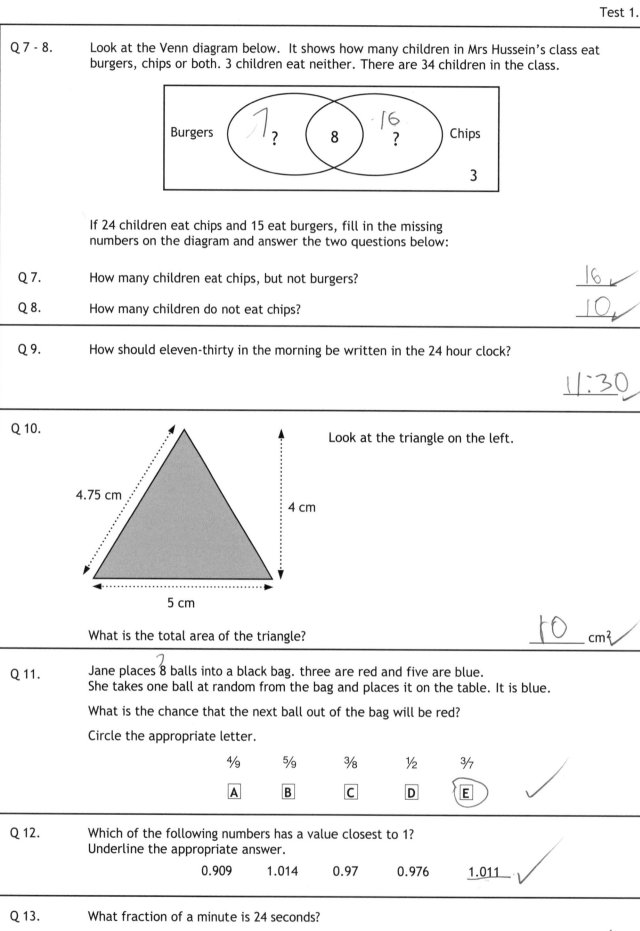

Q 7 - 8. Look at the Venn diagram below. It shows how many children in Mrs Hussein's class eat burgers, chips or both. 3 children eat neither. There are 34 children in the class.

Burgers   7   ?   8   16   ?   Chips

3

If 24 children eat chips and 15 eat burgers, fill in the missing numbers on the diagram and answer the two questions below:

Q 7. How many children eat chips, but not burgers?   16 ✓ |

Q 8. How many children do not eat chips?   10 ✓ |

Q 9. How should eleven-thirty in the morning be written in the 24 hour clock?

11:30 ✓

Q 10.

4.75 cm

4 cm

5 cm

Look at the triangle on the left.

What is the total area of the triangle?   10   cm² ✓   4

Q 11. Jane places 8 balls into a black bag. three are red and five are blue.
She takes one ball at random from the bag and places it on the table. It is blue.

What is the chance that the next ball out of the bag will be red?

Circle the appropriate letter.

⁴⁄₉   ⁵⁄₉   ³⁄₈   ½   ³⁄₇

A   B   C   D   (E)   ✓

Q 12. Which of the following numbers has a value closest to 1?
Underline the appropriate answer.

0.909   1.014   0.97   0.976   1.011 ✓

Q 13. What fraction of a minute is 24 seconds?

Write your answer in its lowest possible terms.   2/5 ✓

V.G.   7

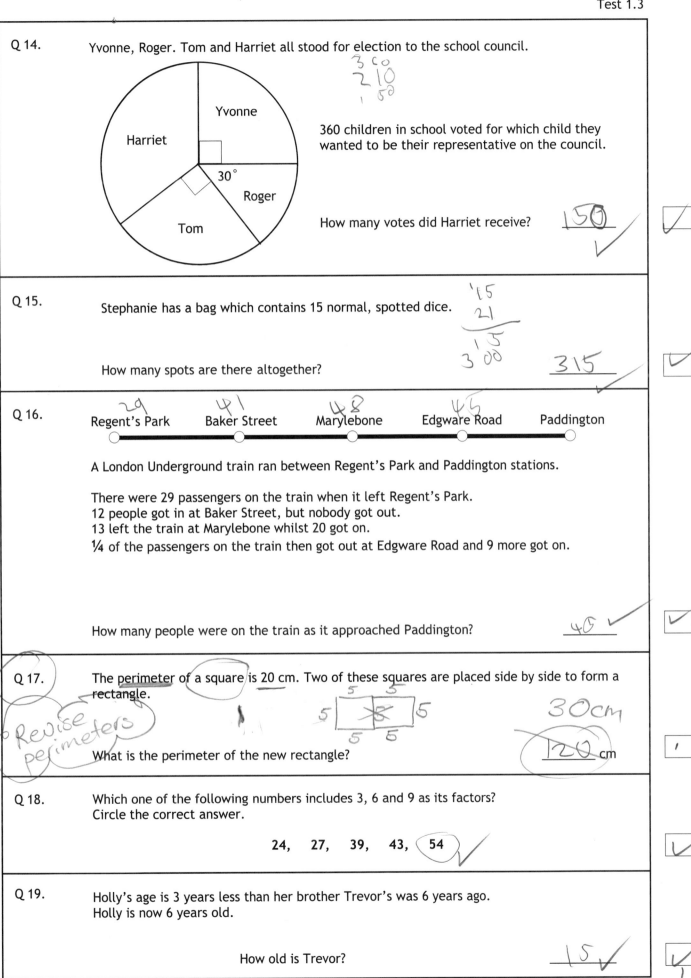

Q 14.
Yvonne, Roger. Tom and Harriet all stood for election to the school council.

Yvonne

Harriet

30°

Roger

Tom

360 children in school voted for which child they wanted to be their representative on the council.

How many votes did Harriet receive? 150 ✓

Q 15.
Stephanie has a bag which contains 15 normal, spotted dice.

How many spots are there altogether? 315 ✓

Q 16.
Regent's Park   Baker Street   Marylebone   Edgware Road   Paddington

A London Underground train ran between Regent's Park and Paddington stations.

There were 29 passengers on the train when it left Regent's Park.
12 people got in at Baker Street, but nobody got out.
13 left the train at Marylebone whilst 20 got on.
¼ of the passengers on the train then got out at Edgware Road and 9 more got on.

How many people were on the train as it approached Paddington? 46 ✓

Q 17.
The perimeter of a square is 20 cm. Two of these squares are placed side by side to form a rectangle.

Revise perimeters

What is the perimeter of the new rectangle? 30cm 20 cm

Q 18.
Which one of the following numbers includes 3, 6 and 9 as its factors?
Circle the correct answer.

24,   27,   39,   43,   54 ✓

Q 19.
Holly's age is 3 years less than her brother Trevor's was 6 years ago.
Holly is now 6 years old.

How old is Trevor? 15 ✓

5/6

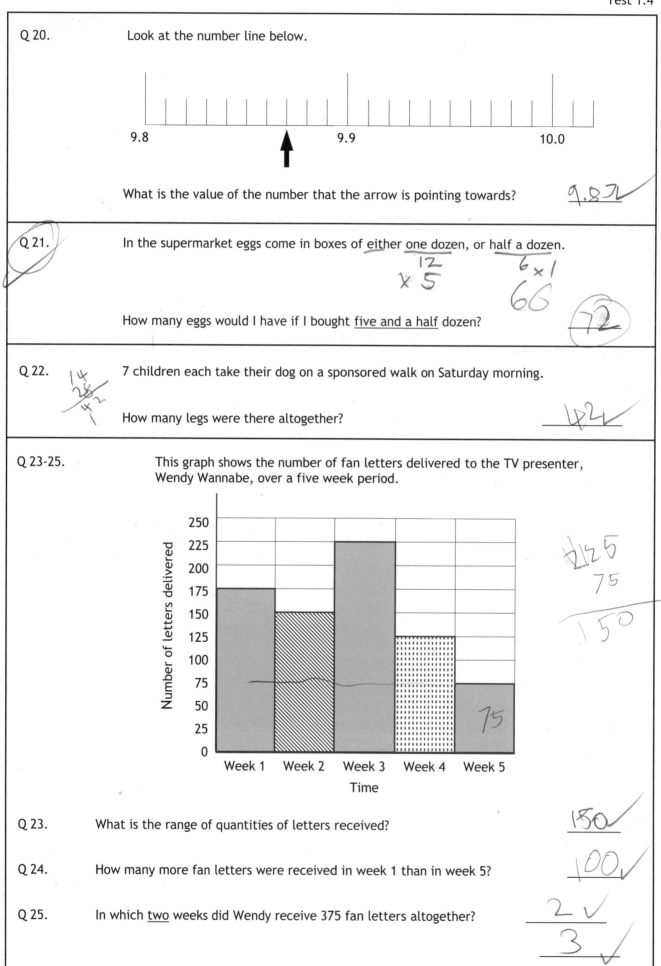

Q 20. Look at the number line below.

9.8   9.9   10.0

What is the value of the number that the arrow is pointing towards? 9.82

Q 21. In the supermarket eggs come in boxes of either one dozen, or half a dozen.

12
x 5   6 x 1

66

How many eggs would I have if I bought five and a half dozen? 72

Q 22. 7 children each take their dog on a sponsored walk on Saturday morning.

14
28
42

How many legs were there altogether? 42

Q 23-25. This graph shows the number of fan letters delivered to the TV presenter, Wendy Wannabe, over a five week period.

125
75

150

Q 23. What is the range of quantities of letters received? 150

Q 24. How many more fan letters were received in week 1 than in week 5? 100

Q 25. In which two weeks did Wendy receive 375 fan letters altogether? 2

3

Q 26.

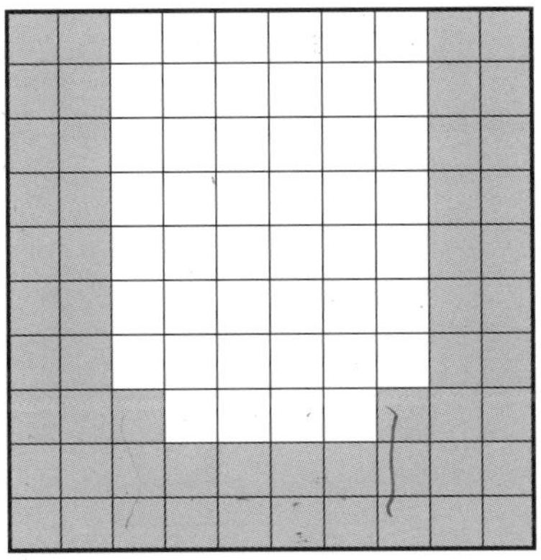

Look carefully at the grid to the left.

What percentage of this grid has been shaded?

$40+6+8 = 54\%$ (46) %

⌐

Q 27.

Jenny has the job of totalling the cheques in her father's shop. Today she has four cheques. £1.99, £7.63, £14.65 and £8.93. How much are the cheques worth in total?

Correct maths.
Incorrect copying of answer

How much are the cheques worth in total?

1.99
7.63
14.65
8.93
33.20   33.20

Q 28.

Which of these shapes has a rotational symmetry of 8?

Circle the appropriate letter.

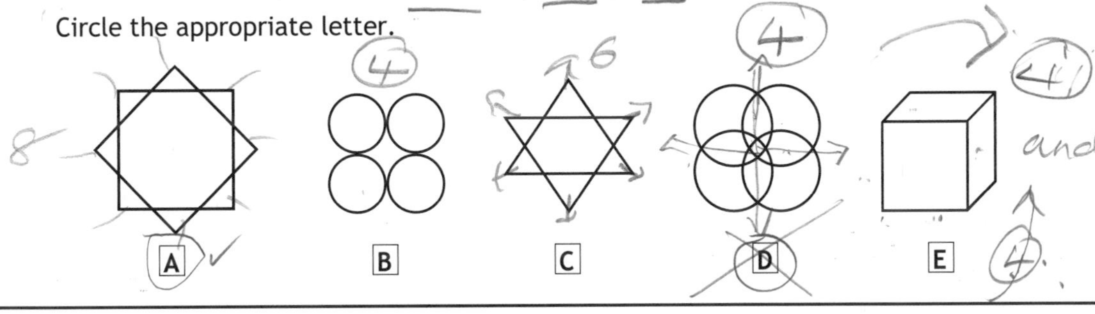

A   B   C   D   E   and.

⌐

Q 29.

Belinda's pet snake weighs 11,006 grams.

What is its weight in Kilograms?

11.006 Kg

☐

Q 30.

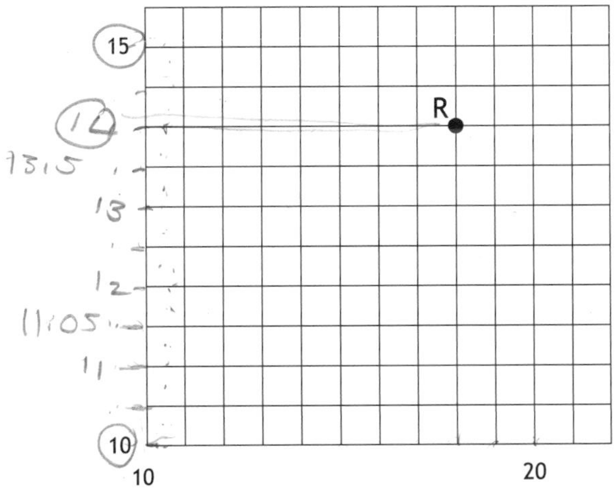

Carefully examine the grid to the left.

80%.

Well done
14
(18 (13)

What are the co-ordinates of point R?   (18 , 13)

✓

You are at the end of the test. If you have time, go back and check your work.

| 1 | 5 |

= 80% 24 30

Time Finished 10:38   END   ✓ .G Time taken 23 mins

Homework 12/07/15

11+ Mathematics - Paper 2.

You have 35 minutes to complete this paper.

Time started: 5:02

Q 1. Simon goes to a Judo class once every week.
He pays £1.50 each time he goes.

£1.50
52
─────
200
7 500

How much does he pay in one year? £ 78.00

Q 2.

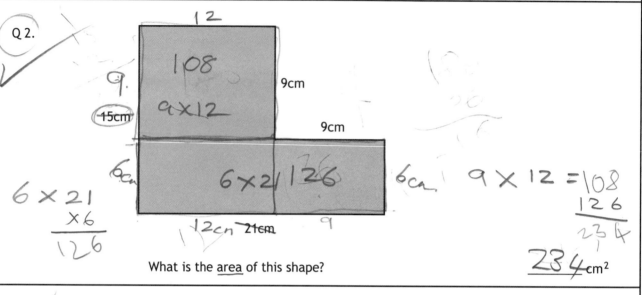

12
108
9. 9×12
(15cm) 9cm
9cm
6×21 126 $9 \times 12 = 108$
126
─────
234

6×21
$\times 6$
─────
126

12cm 21cm

What is the area of this shape? 234 cm²

Q 3. Sally spends **x** pounds each day on her bus journey to and from school.
She spends **y** pounds each weekend on a bus trip to see her grandmother.

How much does Sally spend altogether in 4 weeks? Place a cross in the appropriate box.

A.	20y + 4x	☐
B.	20x + y	☐
C.	5y + 10x	☐
D.	20x + 4y	☒
E.	5x + 4y	☐

Q 4.

18		16
N	15	

This is a magic square.
All the columns, rows and diagonals add up to 45.
Several numbers have been missed out.

What number should replace letter *N*? 13

Q 5. Mrs Nolan bought 352 daffodil bulbs.
They come packed in bags of 16.

16) 352

How many bags of daffodil bulbs did Mrs Nolan buy? 22

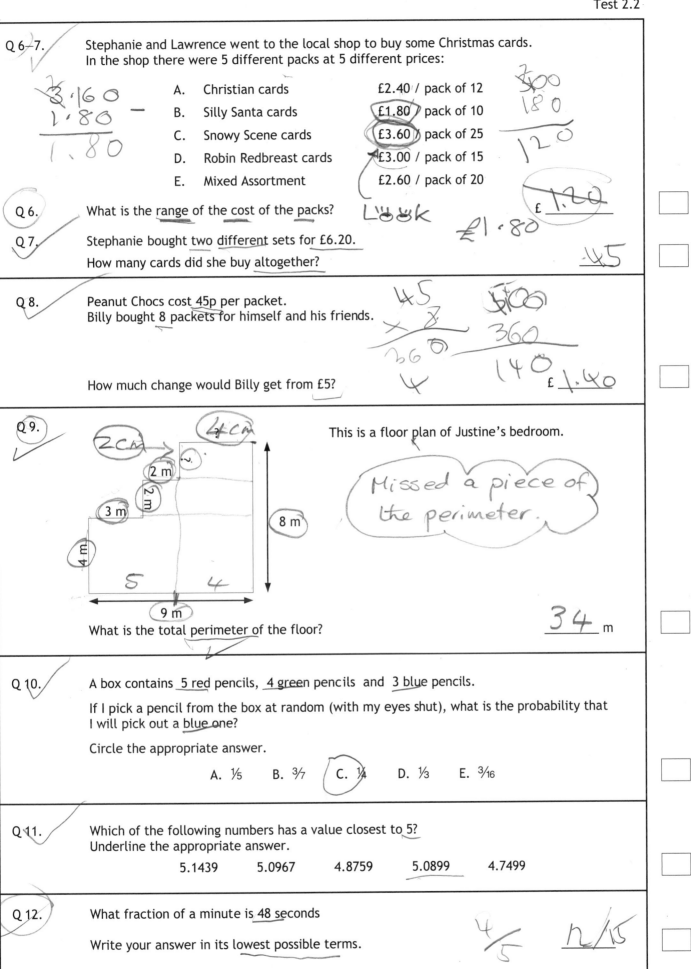

Q 6-7. Stephanie and Lawrence went to the local shop to buy some Christmas cards.
In the shop there were 5 different packs at 5 different prices:

A.	Christian cards	£2.40 / pack of 12
B.	Silly Santa cards	£1.80 / pack of 10
C.	Snowy Scene cards	£3.60 / pack of 25
D.	Robin Redbreast cards	£3.00 / pack of 15
E.	Mixed Assortment	£2.60 / pack of 20

3·60
1·80
—
1·80

300
180
—
120

Q 6. What is the range of the cost of the packs? Look £ 1.80
£1·80

Q 7. Stephanie bought two different sets for £6.20.
How many cards did she buy altogether? 45

Q 8. Peanut Chocs cost 45p per packet.
Billy bought 8 packets for himself and his friends.

45
× 8
360

500
360
—
140

How much change would Billy get from £5? £ 1.40

Q 9. This is a floor plan of Justine's bedroom.

2cm 4cm

2 m
2 m
3 m
4 m
8 m
5
4
9 m

Missed a piece of the perimeter.

What is the total perimeter of the floor? 34 m

Q 10. A box contains 5 red pencils, 4 green pencils and 3 blue pencils.

If I pick a pencil from the box at random (with my eyes shut), what is the probability that I will pick out a blue one?

Circle the appropriate answer.

A. ⅕   B. ³⁄₇   C. ¼   D. ⅓   E. ³⁄₁₆

Q 11. Which of the following numbers has a value closest to 5?
Underline the appropriate answer.

5.1439   5.0967   4.8759   5.0899   4.7499

Q 12. What fraction of a minute is 48 seconds

Write your answer in its lowest possible terms. ⅘ 12/15

7

Q 13. There are 16 small sausage rolls in a pack.

16⟌192 ← 12

How many packs could you make from 192 sausages?   12 packs

Q 14. The local bicycle shop has a great sale.
Every item in the shop is reduced by 50%.
Mike's dad buys the super bike that Mike wants.
It normally costs £350.00.

2⟌350.000 ← 175

How much does Mike's dad have to pay for the bike in the sale?   £ 175.00

Q 15. In the same bicycle shop Mike's sister, Hilary, bought a scooter for £87.50.

87.50
× 2
175.00

What was the price of the scooter BEFORE the sale started?   £ 175.00

Q 16. This diagram shows part of a shape. It shows two of its lines of symmetry.

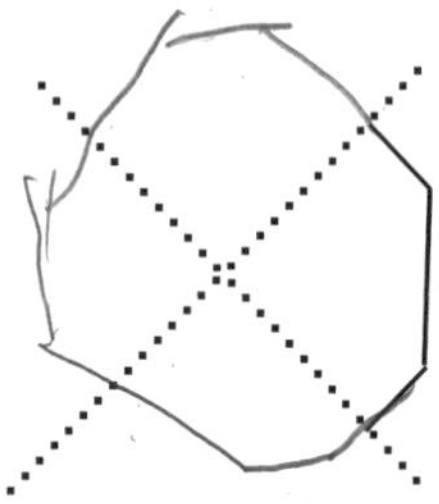

How many sides does the whole shape have?   8

Q 16 - 17.

Trapezium →

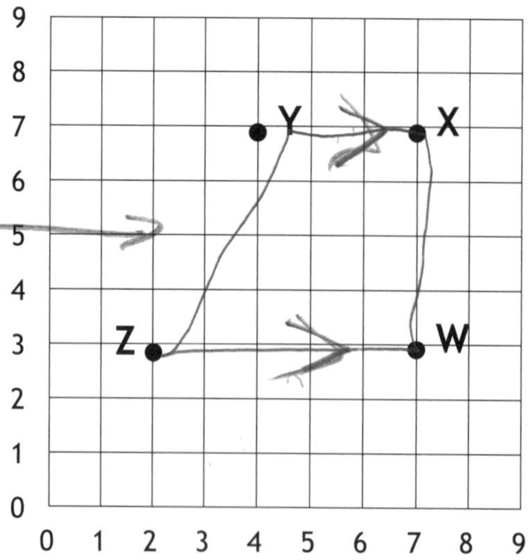

What are the co-ordinates of the points at letter X and letter Z?   X 7, 7
Z 2, 3

Q 17.

Q 18. If you joined the points in alphabetical order, then back to W, what shape would you have drawn?   Kite   trapizium

Q 19. This shape has been created using two identical equilateral triangles.

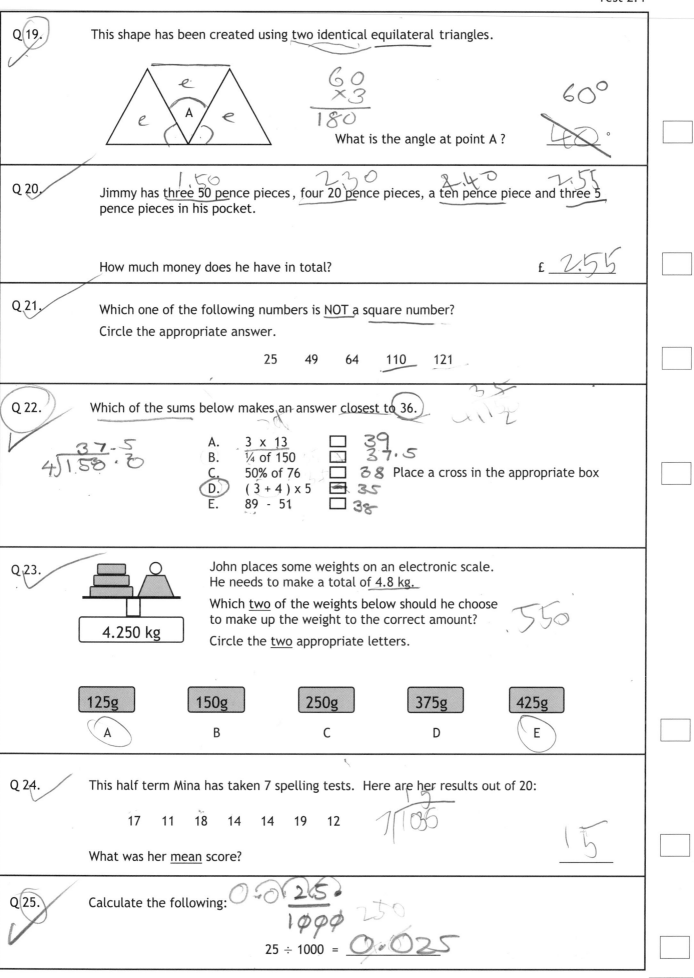

$$\begin{array}{r} 60 \\ \times 3 \\ \hline 180 \end{array}$$

What is the angle at point A ?

60°

~~60~~ °

Q 20. Jimmy has three 50 pence pieces, four 20 pence pieces, a ten pence piece and three 5 pence pieces in his pocket.

1.50   230   2.40   2.55

How much money does he have in total?   £ 2.55

Q 21. Which one of the following numbers is NOT a square number?

Circle the appropriate answer.

25   49   64   110   121

Q 22. Which of the sums below makes an answer closest to 36.

$$4\overline{)158 \cdot 0}\ \ 37.5$$

A.   3 x 13   ☐ 39
B.   ¼ of 150   ☐ 37.5
C.   50% of 76 ☐ 38   Place a cross in the appropriate box
D.   (3 + 4) x 5 ☒ 35
E.   89 - 51   ☐ 38

Q 23.

John places some weights on an electronic scale.
He needs to make a total of 4.8 kg.

Which two of the weights below should he choose
to make up the weight to the correct amount?   550

4.250 kg

Circle the two appropriate letters.

| 125g | 150g | 250g | 375g | 425g |
| A | B | C | D | E |

Q 24. This half term Mina has taken 7 spelling tests. Here are her results out of 20:

17   11   18   14   14   19   12 $7\overline{)105}$

What was her mean score?   15

Q 25. Calculate the following: $\dfrac{25}{1000}$ 250

25 ÷ 1000 = 0.025

7

Q 26.

In a supermarket, there 567 boxes of eggs.
78 are used in the supermarket Cafe.
365 are sold to members of the public.

How many boxes remain unsold?

78
365
443
1 1

567
443
124

124

Q 27.

Peter's grandma is 5 times as old as Peter was 3 years ago.

If Peter's grandma is 55, how old is Peter?

14

Q 28.

slip up

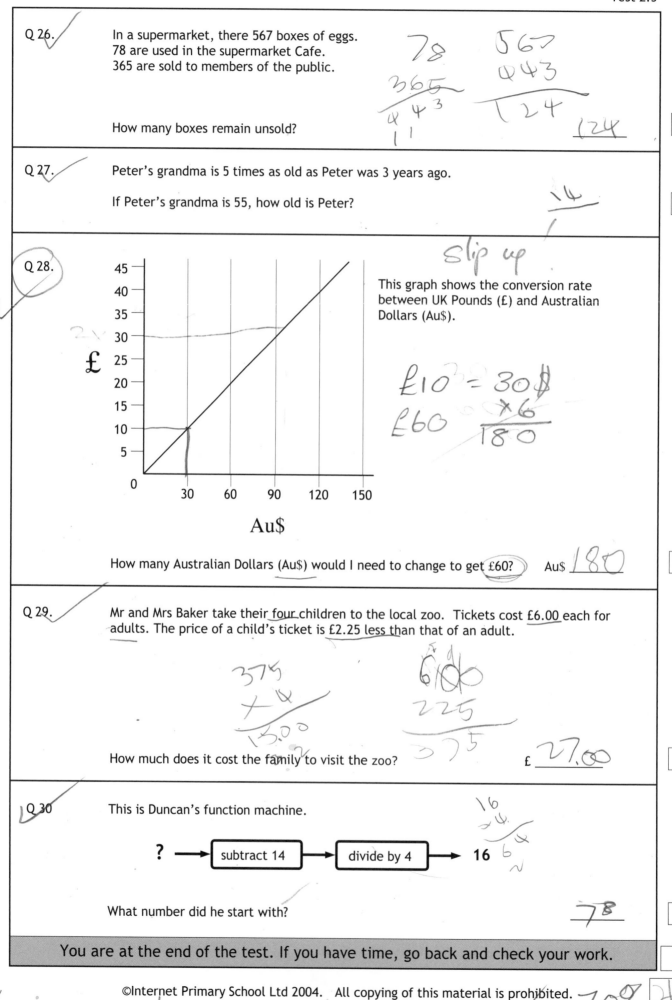

This graph shows the conversion rate between UK Pounds (£) and Australian Dollars (Au$).

£10 = 30$
£60   × 6
        180

How many Australian Dollars (Au$) would I need to change to get £60?   Au$ 180

Q 29.

Mr and Mrs Baker take their four children to the local zoo. Tickets cost £6.00 each for adults. The price of a child's ticket is £2.25 less than that of an adult.

375
× 4
15.00

6.00
225
375

How much does it cost the family to visit the zoo?   £ 27.00

Q 30

This is Duncan's function machine.

16
4
× 4
6
2

? ⟶ [subtract 14] ⟶ [divide by 4] ⟶ 16

What number did he start with?

78

You are at the end of the test. If you have time, go back and check your work.

70%

Time completed: 5.41   Time taken: 39   Good! 70%

11+ Mathematics - Paper 3.

You have 35 minutes to complete this paper.

Q 1.   What is this number to 2 decimal places?

67.3597612   *57.36*

Q 2.   Which of these shapes has the longest perimeter?

Circle the appropriate letter.

4 cm — A (*16*)

3 cm — B (*15*)

6 cm, 4 cm — C (*18*)

4 cm — D (*16*)

3 cm — E (*18*)

Q 3.   What fraction of the months of the year have 31 days?

Write your answer in its lowest possible terms.   *7/12*

Q 4.   Find the missing number so that the equation balances.

$4 \times 6 + 13 = 3 \times 5 + \underline{22}$ (*24*, *37*)

Q 5.

8   4   2
8
8   4

=4cm²

Look at the net to the left.

When folded it makes a box.

```
  40
 x 4
 160
```

If the side of each small square is 2 cm,
what will be the total surface area of the box?   *160* cm²

Q 6.   Milk can be bought in plastic containers, small, medium and large.
If 4 large containers hold as much as 6 medium containers, which of the following
statements MUST be true?

Tick the appropriate box.

$\frac{4}{8} = \frac{6}{12}$ 4:6
                               12:18

16   24

2	3
4	6
8	12
16	24

A.   Large containers hold 2 litres.   ☐
B.   12 large containers hold as much as 18 medium containers.   ☐
C.   12 medium containers hold as much as 6 large.   ☐
D.   Small containers hold 1 litre.   ☐
E.   8 large containers hold as much as 16 medium containers.   ☐

6

H/W

Test 3.2

Q 7–8.   Ahmed and Lorenzo went to the local shop to buy some coloured drawing pencils.
In the stationery shop there were 5 different packs at 5 different prices:

A.   School Pack Pencils   £2.35 / pack
B.   Deluxe Pencils   £3.10 / pack
C.   Artista Pencils   £3.60 / pack
D.   Econo Pencils   £1.50 / pack
E.   ColourBrite Pencils   £2.65 / pack

3.60
4.50
2.10

Q 7.   ✓   What is the range of prices of the packs?   £ *2.10*

Q 8.   Lorenzo bought two different sets for £5.10.
Which **two** did he buy?   Write the two appropriate letters.   *C* and *D*

Q 9.   Minty Chews cost 27p per packet.
Billy bought 6 packets for himself and his friends.

27
× 6
162

How much **change** would Billy get from a £2 coin?   £ *0.38*

Q 10.

4.5
9 cm²
3 cm
3 cm
2 m²

4 m

2 m
1.5 m
1 m
1 m
1 m

2 m

This is a floor plan of Christopher's bedroom.

14 cm²

What is the total area of the floor?   *10.8* m²

Q 11.   A box contains 3 red pencils, 5 green pencils and 2 blue pencils.

If I pick a pencil from the box at random (with my eyes shut), what is the probability that I will pick out a blue one?

Circle the appropriate answer.

A. ¼   B. 2/7   C. 1/5   D. ⅓   E. 2/5

Q 12.   Which of the following numbers has a value closest to 10?
Underline the appropriate answer.

9.0967   10.1439   9.8763   9.7439   10.0967

967
+ 19,000

Q 13.   What fraction of an hour is 36 minutes?

Write your answer in its lowest possible terms.

36/60 = 6/10 = 3/5

©Internet Primary School Ltd 2004.   All copying of this material is prohibited.

$$30 \overline{) 23.2020} \quad 0.766\dot{6}$$

Q 14. Jenny's mum takes Jenny and her three friends
to the cinema as a 10th birthday treat.
It costs £4.00 for adults and £2.50 each for children.
Each girl also has an ice-cream and Jenny's mum has a cup of tea.
Ice-creams are £1.20 each and cups of tea cost £1.30.

How much does it cost Jenny's mum altogether?

£ 20.10

$$2.50 \times 4 = 10.00$$
$$1.20 \times 4$$
$$4.80$$
$$1.30$$
$$6.10$$

14

Q 15. The ratio of flour to sugar in a cake is 5 : 3.

If 300g of sugar was used to make the cake, how much flour was used?

500 g

Q 16. The product of 2 numbers is 96.
The difference between the two numbers is 4.

What are the two numbers?

8 and 12

Q 17.

Look at the shape on the left.

The area of the shaded triangle is 56 cm².

What is the area of the whole shape?

336 cm²

56
6
6
3

Q 18. Justine adds her age to her sister Rowena's age. Between them they are the same age as their uncle Phil. Rowena is 4 years older than Justine. Uncle Phil is 34.

How old is Justine?

15

Q 19.

The hands of the classroom clock show the time 4 o'clock.

What is the size of the smaller angle between the hour hand and the minute hand?

120 °

6

Q 20. This shape has been created using two identical equilateral triangles.

360
120
240

What is the size of angle A ?   170 °

Q 21. Joseph has two 50 pence pieces, three 20 pence pieces, a ten pence piece and three 5 pence pieces in his pocket.

100   160   170

How much money does he have in total?   £ 1.85

Q 22. Which one of the following number is NOT a square number?

Circle the appropriate answer.

36   56   81   121   169

6   49   64

Q 23. I have four sides.
All the sides are of equal length,

I have 2 pairs of angles.
One pair is larger than the other.

What shape am I?   rhombos

Q 24. Eric spends **x** pounds each day on sweets. He spends **y** pounds each week on cds.

How much does Eric spend altogether in one week? Place a cross in the appropriate box.

A. $2y + 5x$ ☐
B. $x + 7y$ ☐
C. $5y + 2x$ ☐
D. $7x + y$ ☒
E. $7x + 7y$ ☐

Q 25. This half term Joan has taken 7 spelling tests. Here are her results out of 20:

17   13   18   15   15   18   18

What was her Median score?   17

Q 26. Dad still talks about buying petrol in gallons.

Approximately how many litres are in a gallon? Circle the appropriate answer.

0.5l   4.5l   8.5l   10l   15l

7

Q 27. Mrs Davison buys a map of Ireland. It is drawn to the of scale 1 : 500,000.

What distance, in kilometres, is represented by 1 cm on the map?
Circle the appropriate letter.

5 km	500 km	50 km	5000 km	500,000 m
A	B	C	D	E

Q 28. Which one of the following shapes will NOT form a letter when reflected in the line A B?

Circle the appropriate letter.

A .... H   C   ⯇   D   E .... B

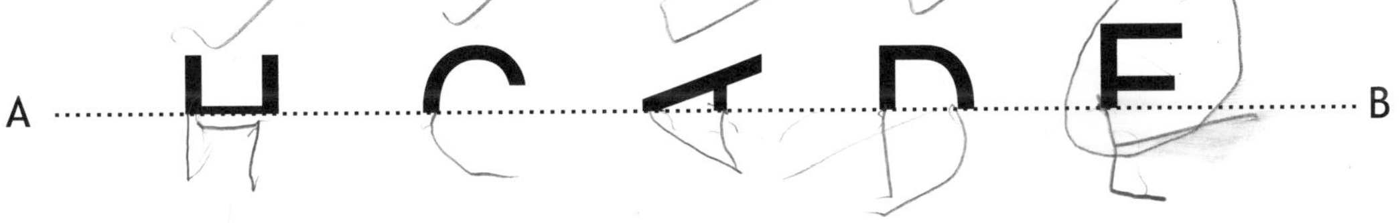

Q 29.

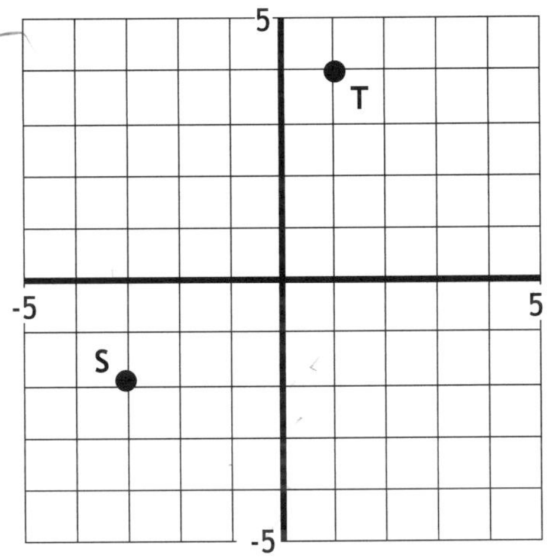

Look at the graph to the left.

Find the co-ordinates of **S** and **T**.

Place a cross in the appropriate box.

	S	T	
A.	(3, 2)	(4, 1)	☐
B.	(-3, 2)	(1, 4)	☐
C.	(-2, - 3)	(4, 1)	☐
D.	(-3, -2)	(1, 4)	☒
E.	(-2, -3)	(-4, 1)	☐

Q 30. Hilary is flying to New York in America to visit her pen friend, Mike.

There is a time difference between Great Britain and the United States.

Hilary's home in London is 5 hours ahead Mike's home in New York.

It takes 7 hours to fly from London to New York.

If Hilary's plane leaves London at 11pm what will the
time be in New York when her plane touches down?

(Remember to state AM or PM)

I AM

| You are at the end of the test. If you have time, go back and check your work. | 4 |

23 30

Time completed: 3:43   Time taken: 28 mins   77?

20:48

11+ Mathematics - Paper 4.

You have 35 minutes to complete this paper.

Q 1. Mr and Mrs Nolan take their four children on a train to the seaside.
The fare normally costs £6.30 for adults and £3.30 for children.
They buy a family ticket which costs £18.00.

£15.90
18.00
07.80

12.60
13.20
25.80

6.30 2. 3.30
26.0 4
12.6° 13.20

How much do they save? £ 780

Q 2.

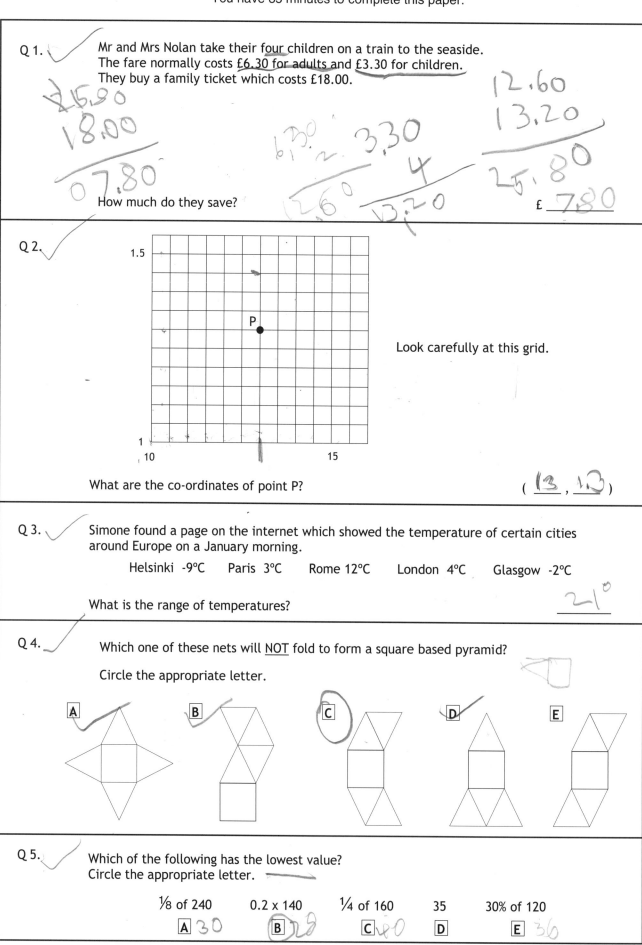

Look carefully at this grid.

What are the co-ordinates of point P? (13 , 13)

Q 3. Simone found a page on the internet which showed the temperature of certain cities around Europe on a January morning.

Helsinki -9°C   Paris 3°C   Rome 12°C   London 4°C   Glasgow -2°C

What is the range of temperatures? 21°

Q 4. Which one of these nets will **NOT** fold to form a square based pyramid?

Circle the appropriate letter.

A   B   C   D   E

Q 5. Which of the following has the lowest value?
Circle the appropriate letter.

⅛ of 240   0.2 x 140   ¼ of 160   35   30% of 120
A 30   B 28   C 40   D   E 36

5

Q 6. ✓ Chocolate Drops are packed 48 drops to a bag.

$$48\overline{)576}^{12}$$

How many bags would be needed to pack 576 Chocolate Drops? _12_

Q 7. Johnny decides to write a diary during his Summer holiday from school.

His first entry is on 23rd July. (inc) →31 9 days
He makes an entry every day until he goes back to school. 31 +2
His last entry is on September 2nd. (inc)

How many entries did he make in his diary? 42

2
31
9

Q 8. ✓

What percentage of this grid has been shaded? _48_%

Q 9. Belinda's pet snake is 5 feet long. What is this length in centimetres?
Circle the appropriate answer.

100 cm   (150 cm)   200 cm   250 cm   300 cm

Q 10. ✓ Samantha receives £1.60 pocket money per week.
If she saves half of it each week how much
money will she have saved after 12 weeks?

80
12
160
800

£ _9.60_

Q 11. ✓ Catherine and Matthew go to a music club after
school each weekday during the spring term.
They have to pay 80p a day each to attend.
Matthew pays an extra 50p a day to hire a trumpet,
whilst Catherine takes her own trombone.

How much will it cost the pair of them to go to the music club for one week? £ _10.50_

Q 12. ✓ Which one of the following numbers includes 3, 6 and 2 as its factors?
Circle the appropriate answer.

16,   28,   32,   (42,)   45

7

Q 13. The ratio of _men_ to _women_ in the town choir is 4 : 6. = 10 × 9

There are 40 singers in the choir.   16:24 = 40

How many of them are _women_?   24

Q 14.

Paddington   Edgware Road   Marylebone   Baker Street   Regent's Park
   68   61   72   60

A London Underground train ran between Paddington and Regent's Park stations.

There were 68 passengers on the train when it left Paddington.
7 people got out at Edgware Road, but nobody got on.
22 left the train at Marylebone whilst 33 got on.
¼ of the passengers on the train then got out at Baker Street and 6 more got on.

How many people were on the train as it approached Regent's Park?   60

Q 15. The area of a square is 25 cm².

The dimensions of the square are increased by a factor of 2

10 | 100 | 25 | 5

What is the area of the square now?   × 2   100 cm²

Q 16. 400 children took part in a "Guess the teacher's age"
competition. ⅜ guessed too high. ½ guessed too low.

200
150
450 . 50

How many children guessed the correct age of the teacher?   50

Q 17. The garden centre sells packs of Tulip bulbs.
There are 14 bulbs in every large pack.

27 ½ Why . 28 ?
14 | 378   Yes

How many packs can be made from 378 bulbs?   27

Q 18. Peter, Cindy, Mark and Sharon collected drinks cans for a school recycling project.

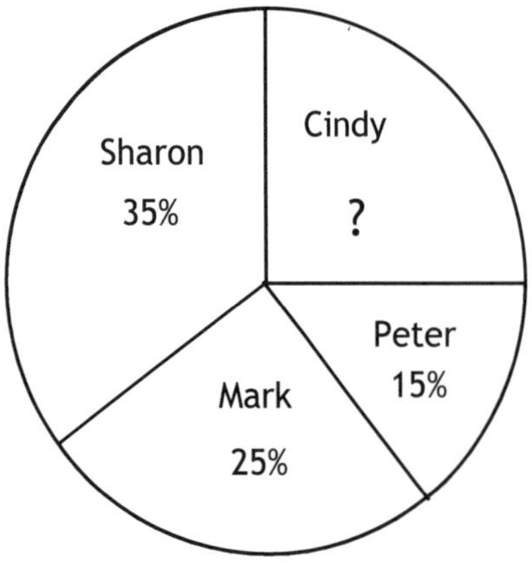

Altogether the four children managed to collect exactly 600 cans. The pie chart on the left shows the percentage collected by each child.

Sharon 35%
Cindy ?
Mark 25%
Peter 15%

How many can did Cindy collect?   150

Q 19. What fraction of 2 minutes is 40 seconds?

$\frac{40}{120} = \frac{4}{12} = \frac{2}{6} = \frac{1}{3}$

Write your answer in its lowest possible terms.

Q 20.

25   26   27

What is the value of the number that the arrow is pointing towards?   26.6

Q 21. Stephanie has a bag which contains 45 normal spotted dice.
How many faces are there altogether which have odd numbers?

45
3
135   135

Q 22–23. Miss Foster's class conducted a survey in their school on the children's favourite foods.

Favourite Foods	
Key: ▣ stands for 6 children ▪ stands for 3 children	
Vegi Burger	▣ ▪
Fish Fingers	▣ ▣ ▣ ▣ ▣ ▪ 33
Pizza	▣ ▣ ▣
Sausages	▣ ▣ 12
Chips	▣ ▣ ▣ ▣ ▪

Q 22. How many children said chips were their favourite?   27

Q 23. How many more children prefer fish fingers to sausages?   21

Q 24. The perimeter of a square is 24 cm.
Two of these squares are placed side by side to form a rectangle.

What is the perimeter of the new rectangle?   36 cm

Q 25. Spiders have 8 legs and ants have two less.
How many legs would there be altogether on 9 ants and 7 spiders?

56
54
110

Q 26. This is a map of the secret passages under Thropton Manor. You must try to find your way from the Hall to the Kitchen using a set of instructions.

Key to the instructions:
FD means forward, **RT** means turn right 90° and **LT** means turn left 90°.

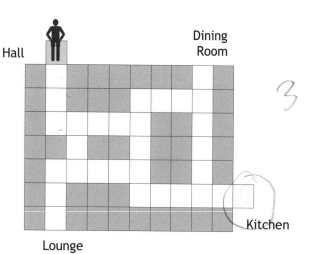

Which of these sets of instructions is the correct one?
Circle the correct letter.

A   FD 4, LT, FD 4, LT, FD 4, LT, FD 3.

B.   FD 3, RT, FD 4, LT, FD 3, LT, FD 5.

C.   FD 2, LT, FD 3, RT, FD 5, RT, FD 3.

D.   FD 3, LT, FD 4, RT, FD 3, LT, FD 5.

E.   FD 4, RT, FD 3, LT, FD 5, RT, FD 3.

Q 27. How should 17.30 be written in the 12 hour clock?   5.30pm

---

Q 28. If $6t + 5 = 23$ what is the value of t?

t = ___3___

Q 29. A map of the island of Tremus is drawn using a scale of 1 : 250,000.
What distance, in metres, is represented by 1 cm on the map?
Circle the appropriate letter.

25,000 m	250 m	2,500 m	250,000 m	2,500,000 m
A	B	C	D	E

Q 30.

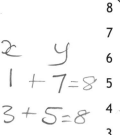

$$\begin{array}{cc} x & y \\ 1 + 7 = 8 \\ 3 + 5 = 8 \end{array}$$

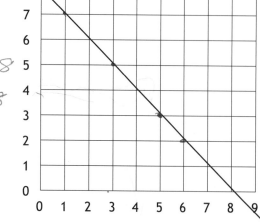

What is the rule that governs the plotting of line A?

Circle the appropriate letter.

A.   X x Y = 4

B.   X - Y = 8

C.   2X = Y + 4

D.   X + Y = 8

E.   2X = 2Y - 8

You are at the end of the test. If you have time, go back and check your work.

5

24 30

37 mins   END   80%

11+ Mathematics - Paper 5.

You have 35 minutes to complete this paper.

1.50

Q 1. ✓ Pamela goes to a dancing class <u>once</u> every week.
She pays £1.80 each time she goes.

How much does she pay in one year?

£1.80
x 52
3.60
90.00   £ 93.60

Q 2. ✓

A

B

C

D

E

Which of these shapes has more than one obtuse angle?

Circle the appropriate letter.

Q 3.   Mr and Mrs Jackman take their <u>four</u> children to the
Wacky Burger Bar. Wacky meals cost £6.00 each for adults.
The price of a child's Wacky meal is £1.80 less than that of an <u>adult</u>.

£28.80

6.00
4.20

4.20

lost   Why?

12.00
6.00
2.800

6.00
1.80
4.20

How much does it cost the family to eat at the Wacky Burger Bar?   £ 28.00

Q 4. ✓   Which of these sets of numbers contains only numbers from the 8 times table?

A.	16	40	66	☐
B.	56	72	84	☐
C.	48	64	96	☒
D.	66	74	108	☐
E.	72	116	144	☐

Place a cross in the appropriate box.

Q 5. ✓   Farouk, Brenda, Martin, Jean and Cassie each
bought a CD from the local music shop.

Farouk paid £7.05, Martin £6.30, Brenda £11.95,
Cassie £10.90 and Jean £9.20.

What was the range of the prices of the CDs?

11.95
6.30

5.65   £ 5.65

5

Q 6—8.   This graph shows the number of bags of crisps sold by the school tuck shop in a five week period.

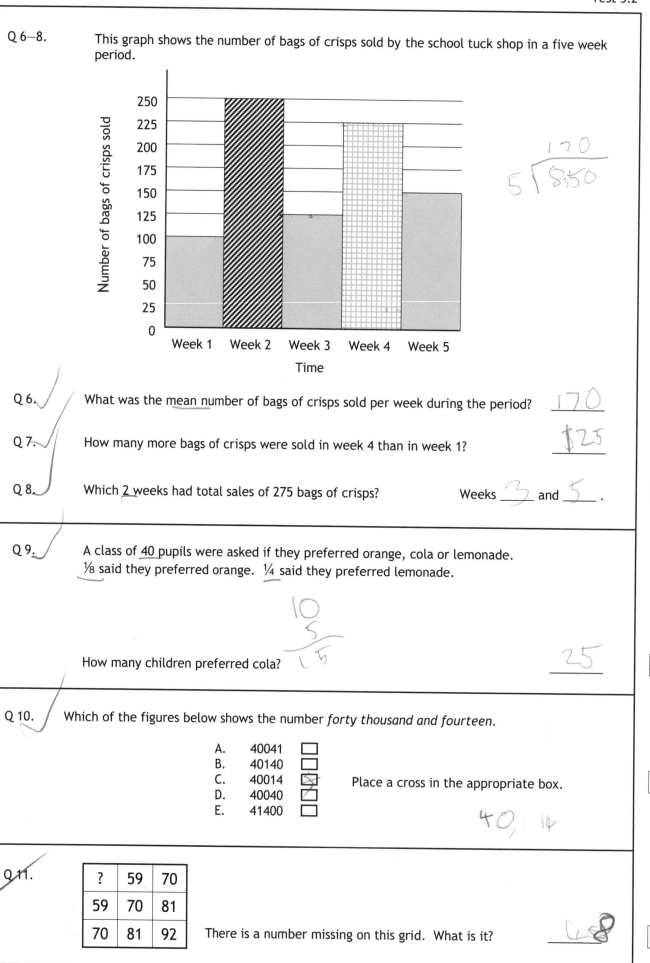

170

5 ⟌ 8̶5̶0

Q 6.   What was the mean number of bags of crisps sold per week during the period?   *170*

Q 7.   How many more bags of crisps were sold in week 4 than in week 1?   *$25*

Q 8.   Which 2 weeks had total sales of 275 bags of crisps?   Weeks *3* and *5* .

Q 9.   A class of 40 pupils were asked if they preferred orange, cola or lemonade. ⅛ said they preferred orange. ¼ said they preferred lemonade.

10
5
15

How many children preferred cola?   *25*

Q 10.   Which of the figures below shows the number *forty thousand and fourteen*.

A.   40041   ☐
B.   40140   ☐
C.   40014   ☒   Place a cross in the appropriate box.
D.   40040   ☐
E.   41400   ☐

40, 14

Q 11.

?	59	70
59	70	81
70	81	92

There is a number missing on this grid. What is it?   *48*

6

Q 12. The local clothes has shop a mega sale.
Every item in the shop is reduced by 25%.
Tina buys the designer top she wants.
It normally costs £18.00.

How much does Tina have to pay for the top in the sale? £ _13.50_ ☐

Q 13. In the sports department of the same clothes
shop Tina's brother, Dave, bought a Premier
League football shirt for £36.00.

What was the price of the shirt BEFORE the sale started? £ _48.00_ ☐

Q 14. Which of these shapes has a rotational symmetry of 5?

Circle the appropriate letter.

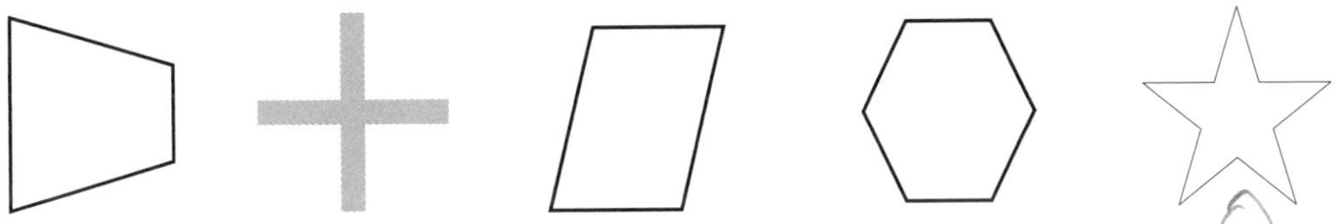

A   B   C   D   (E) ☐

Q 15. There are 18 chocolate bars in a packet. 18/162
How many packets could you make from 162 chocolate bars?

_9_ packets ☐

Q 16. There are 40 children in a class. 26 girls and 14 boys.
One child's name is chosen at random to read a poem in school assembly.

What is the chance that the child will be a boy?

Write your answer as a fraction in its lowest possible terms. _7/20_ ☐

Q 17. This diagram shows part of a shape, and two of its lines of symmetry.

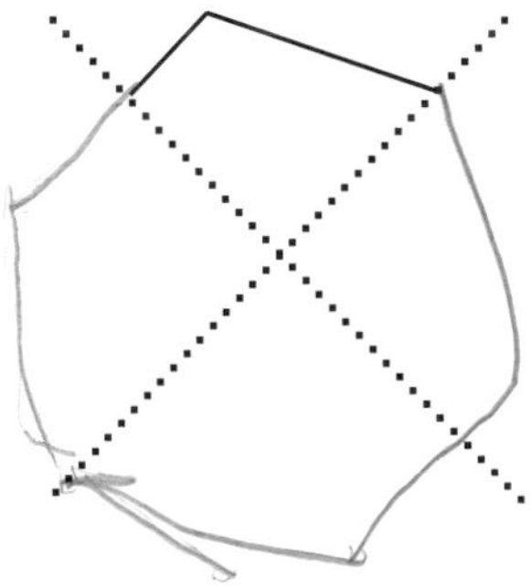

What is the name of the whole shape?

hexagon ☐

6

Q 18. What fraction of a day is 8 hours?

8/24
4/1²
Write you answer in its lowest possible terms. 2 6   1/3

Q 19. If $8t + 5 = 37$, then what is the value of t?

32 $t = $ 4

Q 20—21.

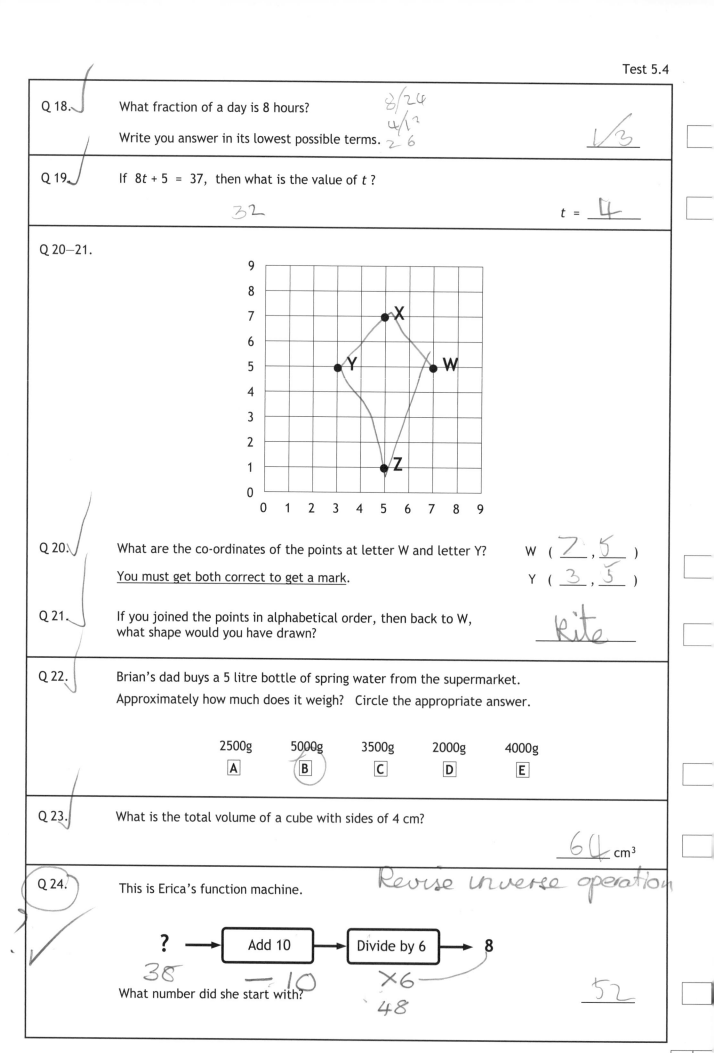

Q 20. What are the co-ordinates of the points at letter W and letter Y?   W (7 , 5)

You must get both correct to get a mark.   Y (3 , 5)

Q 21. If you joined the points in alphabetical order, then back to W,
what shape would you have drawn?   kite

Q 22. Brian's dad buys a 5 litre bottle of spring water from the supermarket.

Approximately how much does it weigh?   Circle the appropriate answer.

2500g	5000g	3500g	2000g	4000g
A	B	C	D	E

Q 23. What is the total volume of a cube with sides of 4 cm?

64 cm³

Q 24. This is Erica's function machine.

Revise inverse operation

? → Add 10 → Divide by 6 → 8

38   — 10   ×6   52
What number did she start with?   48

36 ✗ 9
0
12

Q 25. Three corners of a rectangle have the co-ordinates (2, 1) (7, 8) and (2, 8).

What are the co-ordinates of the fourth corner?   (_7_ , _1_)

Q 26.

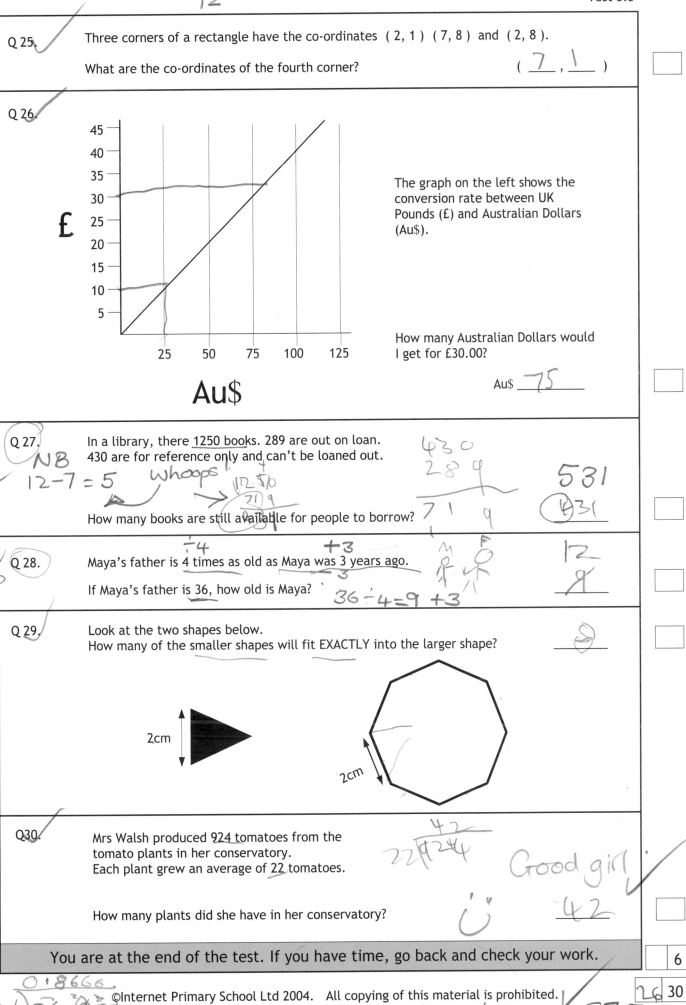

The graph on the left shows the conversion rate between UK Pounds (£) and Australian Dollars (Au$).

How many Australian Dollars would I get for £30.00?

Au$ _75_

Q 27. In a library, there 1250 books. 289 are out on loan. 430 are for reference only and can't be loaned out.

NB
12 - 7 = 5   whoops!

How many books are still available for people to borrow?

430
289

531
(531)

Q 28. Maya's father is 4 times as old as Maya was 3 years ago.

If Maya's father is 36, how old is Maya?   36 ÷ 4 = 9 + 3

Q 29. Look at the two shapes below.
How many of the smaller shapes will fit EXACTLY into the larger shape?

2cm

2cm

Q30. Mrs Walsh produced 924 tomatoes from the tomato plants in her conservatory.
Each plant grew an average of 22 tomatoes.

How many plants did she have in her conservatory?

Good girl

42

You are at the end of the test. If you have time, go back and check your work.   6

26 30

Much better. 87%

11+ Mathematics - Paper 6.

You have 35 minutes to complete this paper.

7.05

Q 1. Simon goes to a Holiday Club every weekday for four weeks during the holidays.
He pays £0.80 each time he goes.

How much does he pay in total during the holiday?

£ 16.00

Q 2.

What is the area of this shape? 75 cm²

78~3

Q 3. Yvonne spends **y** pounds each day on her lunch at school.
She spends **x** pounds each week on a bus pass to get her to and from school

How much does Yvonne spend altogether in 4 weeks? Place a cross in the appropriate box.

A.   20**x** + 4**y**   ☐
B.   5**x** + **y**   ☐
C.   4**y** + 5**x**   ☐
D.   20**y** + 4**x**   ☒
E.   4**x** + 5**y**   ☐

Q 4. Mrs Jackson bought 450 party hats for the school Christmas party.
They come packed in boxes of 18.

How many boxes of party hats did Mrs Jackson buy?

18) 4 5 0

Q 5. This is a magic square.
All the columns, rows and diagonals add up to 45.
Several numbers have been missed out.

18		16
	15	
	P	

What number should replace letter P?

Please write your calculations.

3 4 15 / 26 / 19

5

$9 \times 6 = 54$
$+2 = 11$

H/W   Twx?

Q 6.

In a supermarket, there 438 boxes of Crunchy Flakes breakfast cereal.
59 are sent to another supermarket who have run out.
228 are sold to the public at £1.21 a box.

How many boxes remain unsold?

Q 7.

Nathan's grandpa is 6 times as old as Nathan was 2 years ago.

If Nathan's grandpa is 54, how old is Nathan?   10

Q 8.

This shape has been created using two identical equilateral triangles.   60°

Angles on a straight line add up to 180°

What is the size of angle B ?   300 .°

Q 9.

Mr and Mrs Perkins take their four children to the local theme park. Tickets cost £8.00
each for adults. The price of a child's ticket is £2.50 less than that of an adult.

How much does it cost the family to visit the theme park?   £ 38

Q 10.

This is Gillian's function machine.

? ⟶ [subtract 9] ⟶ [divide by 9] ⟶ 8

What number did she start with?   81

Q 11.

This spinner has an equal chance of landing on any
of the numbers.

What is the chance that it will come to rest on a
number that is a multiple of 8?

56   84
40   96
74   64

Write your answer as a fraction in its lowest possible terms.   2/3

6

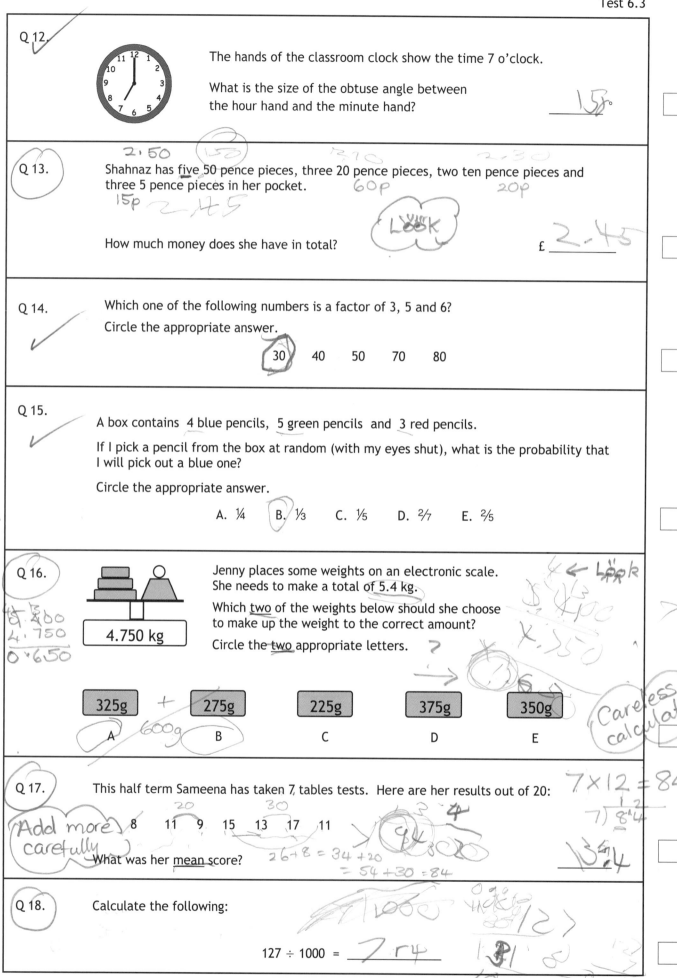

Q 12.

The hands of the classroom clock show the time 7 o'clock.

What is the size of the obtuse angle between the hour hand and the minute hand?

_____ 15°°

Q 13.

2·50

Shahnaz has five 50 pence pieces, three 20 pence pieces, two ten pence pieces and three 5 pence pieces in her pocket.

60p   20p

15p 2·45

Look

How much money does she have in total?

£ _____ 2·45

Q 14.

Which one of the following numbers is a factor of 3, 5 and 6?

Circle the appropriate answer.

(30)   40   50   70   80

Q 15.

A box contains 4 blue pencils, 5 green pencils and 3 red pencils.

If I pick a pencil from the box at random (with my eyes shut), what is the probability that I will pick out a blue one?

Circle the appropriate answer.

A. ¼   (B.) ⅓   C. ⅕   D. 2/7   E. 2/5

Q 16.

Jenny places some weights on an electronic scale. She needs to make a total of 5.4 kg.

Which two of the weights below should she choose to make up the weight to the correct amount?

Circle the two appropriate letters.

← Look

5·400
4·750
0·650

4.750 kg

325g	+	275g		225g		375g		350g
(A)	600g	B		C		D		E

Careless calculation

Q 17.

This half term Sameena has taken 7 tables tests. Here are her results out of 20:

7×12=84

20   30

8   11   9   15   13   17   11

Add more carefully

What was her mean score?

26+8 = 34 +20
= 54 +30 =84

12
7)8 4

12⁴

Q 18.

Calculate the following:

127 ÷ 1000 = _____ 7 r4

7

Q 19.   What fraction of an hour is 36 minutes?

Write your answer in its lowest possible terms.   3/5

Q 20.   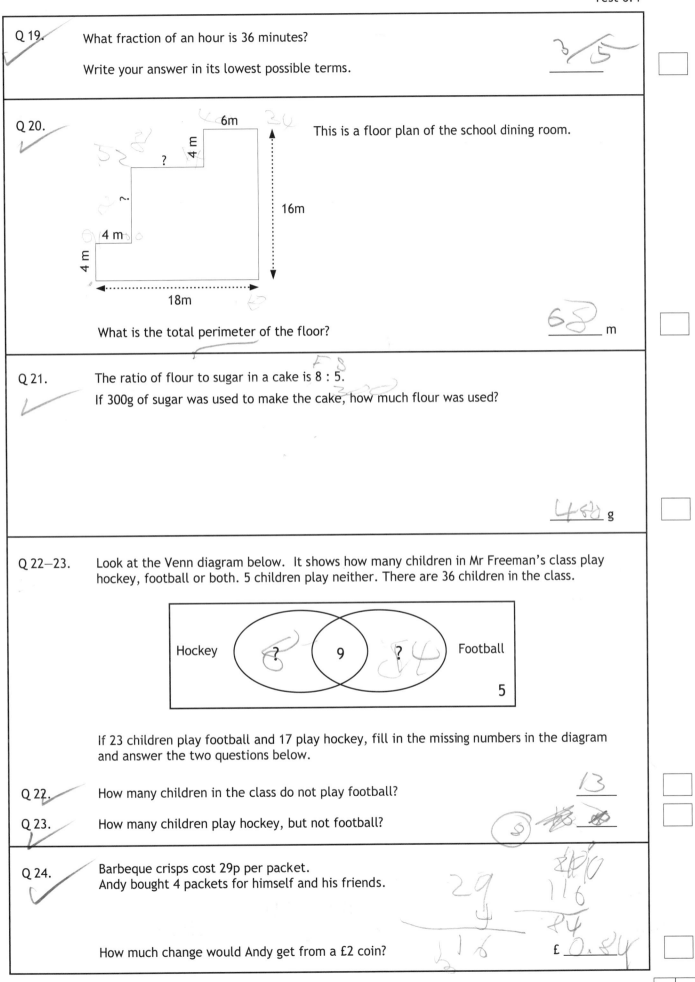   This is a floor plan of the school dining room.

6m

4 m

?

16m

4 m

4 m

18m

What is the total perimeter of the floor?   68 m

Q 21.   The ratio of flour to sugar in a cake is 8 : 5.

If 300g of sugar was used to make the cake, how much flour was used?

480 g

Q 22–23.   Look at the Venn diagram below. It shows how many children in Mr Freeman's class play hockey, football or both. 5 children play neither. There are 36 children in the class.

Hockey   ?   9   ?   Football

5

If 23 children play football and 17 play hockey, fill in the missing numbers in the diagram and answer the two questions below.

Q 22.   How many children in the class do not play football?   13

Q 23.   How many children play hockey, but not football?   8

Q 24.   Barbeque crisps cost 29p per packet.
Andy bought 4 packets for himself and his friends.

29
4
116

How much change would Andy get from a £2 coin?   £ 0.84

6

$30\overline{)200}$ 0.66

H/w

24

$14\overline{)336}$

Q 25. There are 14 chocolate mini-rolls in a pack.

How many packs could you make from 336 mini-rolls? _____24_____ packs

14

Q 26. The local toy shop has a sale.
Every item in the shop is reduced by 50%.
Sally buys a game for her computer.
It normally costs £28.00.

$\frac{6}{84}$ $\frac{14}{4}$

How much does Sally have to pay for the game in the sale? £ _14_

Q 27. In the same local toy shop Sally's little sister, Rowena, bought some clothes for her doll for £7.50.

What was the price of the doll's clothes BEFORE the sale started? £ _15_

Q 28. How many faces has a hexagonal prism?

6

6 faces

Look

Q 29 - 30.

Tidier writing!
Please.

Tidy writing equals a tidy mind

Q 29. What are the co-ordinates of the points at letter F and letter H?

F _4,2_

H _8,7_

Q 30. If you joined the points in alphabetical order, then back to E, what shape would you have drawn?

trapizium

NB. When your writing is untidy you seem to make more mistakes!

You are at the end of the test. If you have time, go back and check your work.

6

20 / 30

END   28   67%

11+ Mathematics - Paper 7.

You have 35 minutes to complete this paper.

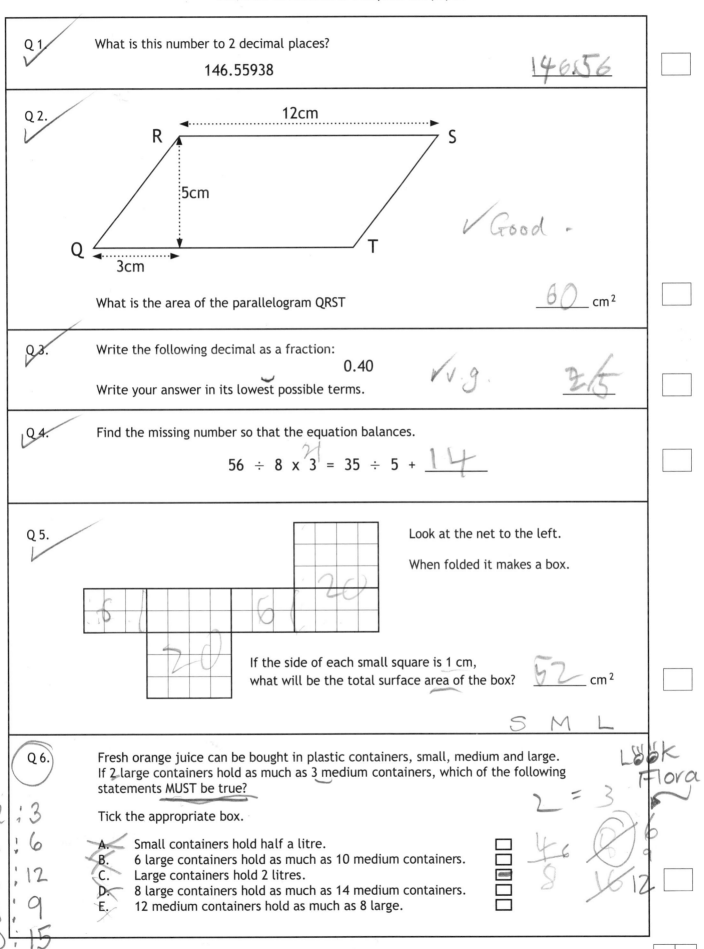

Q 1. What is this number to 2 decimal places?

146.55938

146.56

Q 2.

12cm

R ⎯⎯⎯⎯⎯⎯⎯⎯⎯ S

5cm

Q ⎯ T

3cm

What is the area of the parallelogram QRST

✓ Good .

60 cm²

Q 3. Write the following decimal as a fraction:

0.40

Write your answer in its lowest possible terms.

✓ v.g.

2/5

Q 4. Find the missing number so that the equation balances.

$56 \div 8 \times 3 = 35 \div 5 + \underline{14}$

Q 5. Look at the net to the left.

When folded it makes a box.

20

5   6

20

If the side of each small square is 1 cm,
what will be the total surface area of the box? 52 cm²

S M L

Q 6. Fresh orange juice can be bought in plastic containers, small, medium and large.
If 2 large containers hold as much as 3 medium containers, which of the following
statements MUST be true?

Look
Flora

2 = 3

Tick the appropriate box.

4 6
8

16 12

A. Small containers hold half a litre. ☐
B. 6 large containers hold as much as 10 medium containers. ☐
C. Large containers hold 2 litres. ☐
D. 8 large containers hold as much as 14 medium containers. ☐
E. 12 medium containers hold as much as 8 large. ☐

2 : 3
: 6
: 12
: 9
: 15

6

Q 7. Victoria, Nicky, Anna, John and Peter each buy some food at the local burger bar. Victoria spent £2.49, Nicky £2.30, Anna £3.40, John £3.63 and Peter £1.99. What was the range of amounts spent?

£ 1.64

Q 8. Which of these sets of numbers contains all square numbers?

A. 25 47 56 ☐
B. 36 49 72 ☐
C. 36 64 90 ☐   Place a cross in the appropriate box
D. 48 81 121 ☐
(E.) 121 64 144 ☒

Q 9. Which of these shapes has a rotational symmetry of order 2? Circle the appropriate letter/letters.

Explain rotational symmetry to me again please Flora

A (No)   B   C   D   E

Q 10 - 12. This graph shows the number of merit stars given children in Mrs Blunt's class over a period of a half term.

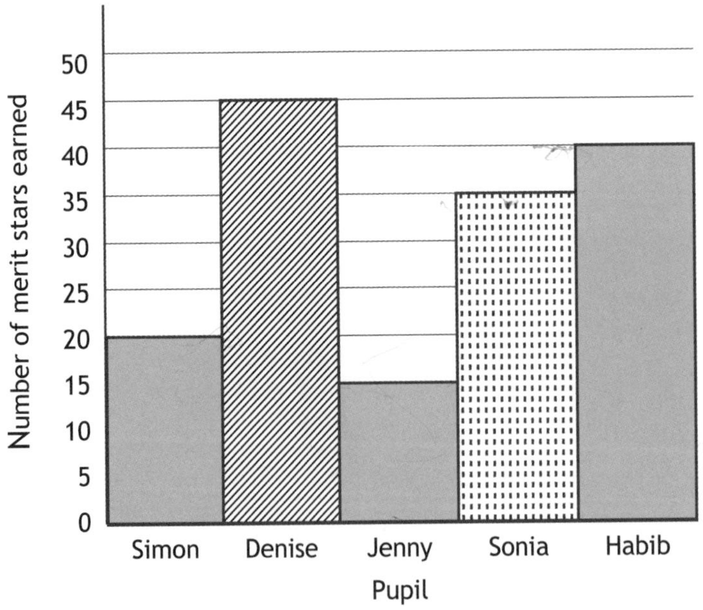

31
5)155

Q 10. What was the mean number of merit stars given per child during this period?   31 ✓

Q 11. How many fewer merits stars did Jenny get than Habib during the period?   25 ✓

Q 12. Which 2 children received a total of 80 merit stars?   *Denise* and *Sonia* ✓

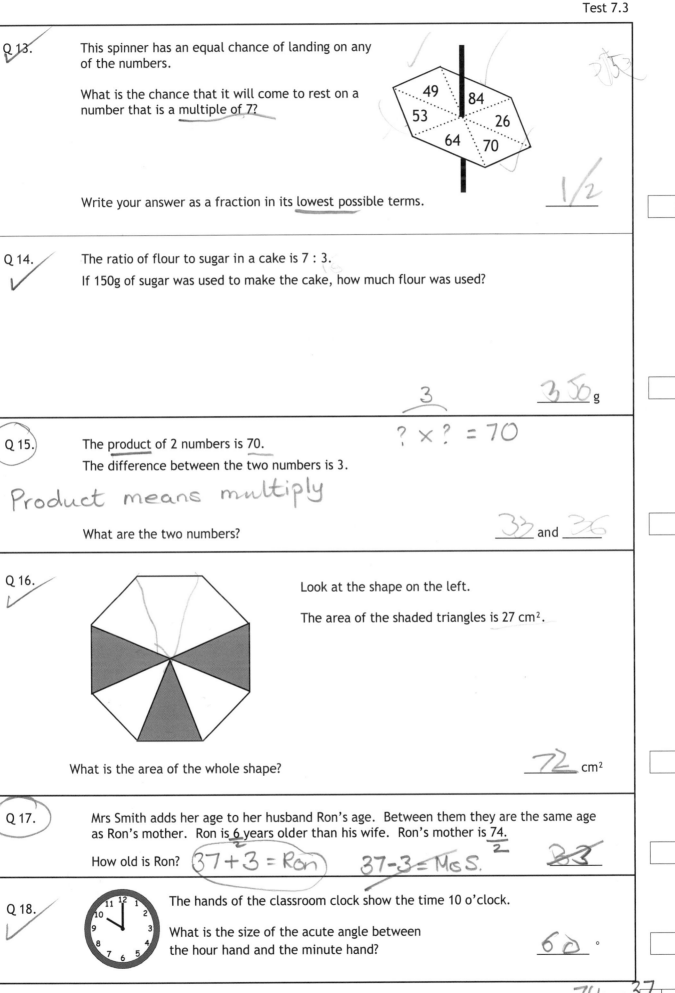

Q 13. This spinner has an equal chance of landing on any of the numbers.

What is the chance that it will come to rest on a number that is a multiple of 7?

49 84
53   26
64 70

Write your answer as a fraction in its lowest possible terms.   1/2

Q 14. The ratio of flour to sugar in a cake is 7 : 3.

If 150g of sugar was used to make the cake, how much flour was used?

$\frac{3}{?}$ 350 g

Q 15. The product of 2 numbers is 70.

? × ? = 70

The difference between the two numbers is 3.

Product means multiply

What are the two numbers?   32 and 36

Q 16.

Look at the shape on the left.

The area of the shaded triangles is 27 cm².

What is the area of the whole shape?   72 cm²

Q 17. Mrs Smith adds her age to her husband Ron's age. Between them they are the same age as Ron's mother. Ron is 6 years older than his wife. Ron's mother is 74.

How old is Ron? 37+3 = Ron   37-3 = Mrs S.   33

Q 18.

The hands of the classroom clock show the time 10 o'clock.

What is the size of the acute angle between the hour hand and the minute hand?   60 °

---

17   S+R = M   S+R = 74   S = R+6 $\frac{74}{2}=37$ $\frac{6}{2}=3$ 6

*Look/Read Twice/Think

Flora! You should n~
make such a simple m~

Test 74

Q 19. Which of the figures below shows the number *forty-four thousand and forty.*

A. 44014 ☒
B. 440040 ☐
C. 44004 ☐   Place a cross in the appropriate box
D. 44040 ☐
E. 4400040 ☐

Q 20. Write down the size of any angle that could appear in an equilateral triangle. __60__ °

Q 21. If 8y - 10 = 46, then what is the value of y ?

y = __7__

Q 22. There are 24 children on a bus. 9 girls and 15 boys.
One child's name is chosen at random to collect the tickets.

B   G
3 ⌐15   9
⌐24   24

Why did you calculate the girls chance?

What is the chance that the child will be a boy?

(Show your answer as a fraction in its lowest terms.)

Q 23. Sam's mum buys a four 1litre bottles of cola from the supermarket.
Approximately how much do they weigh altogether?

(Write your answer in either kilos OR grams) __4000g__

Q 24. What is the volume of a cube with sides of 5 cm?

__125__ cm³

Q 25. Calculate the following:

6.5 ÷ 100 = __0.065__

Q 26. Look at the two shapes below.
How many of the smaller shapes will fit EXACTLY into the larger shape?

2c =

1cm

1cm

2   2

4cm

8

.733
30)22.00

ke

Q 27.   Complete the following number sequence.

5860 0   120   600,   120,   30,   10,   ?
120   30
480   90
                          -480 -90

Not a sequence / think again

x4 x3 x?

Q 28.

Which one of the following shapes has exactly 4 lines of symmetry?

Circle the appropriate letter.

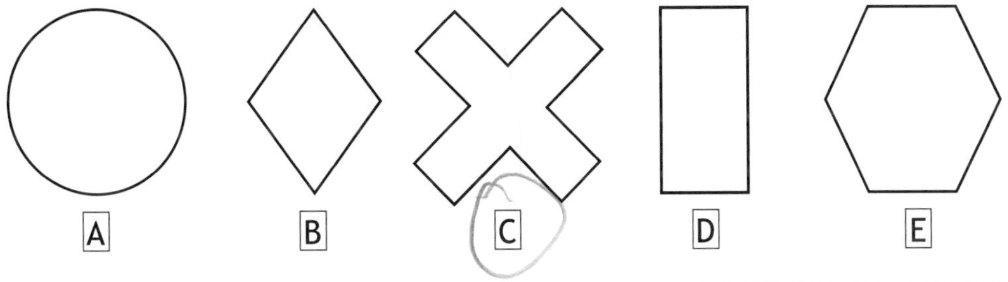

A   B   C   D   E

Q 29.

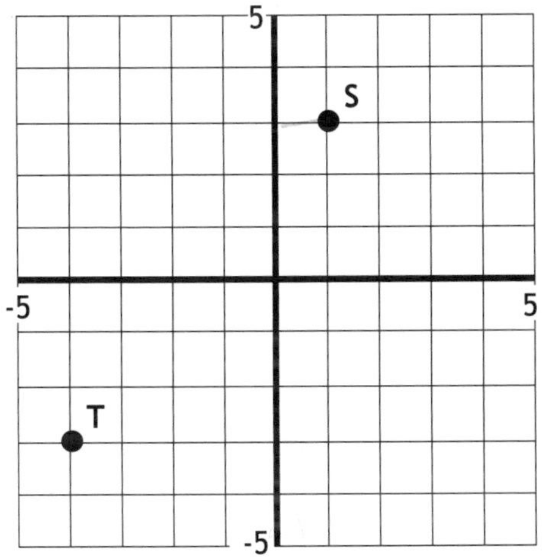

Look at the graph to the left.

Find the co-ordinates of **S** and **T**.

Place a cross in the appropriate box.

S (point on graph)
T (point on graph)

	S	T	
A.	(3, 1)	(-3, -4)	☐
B.	(-3, 1)	(4, -3)	☐
C.	(-1, - 3)	(-3, -4)	☐
D.	(1, 3)	(-4, -3)	☑
E.	(1, -3)	(-4, 3)	☐

Q 30.   Michael is flying to Rovaniemi in Finland to visit his sister, Erica.

There is a time difference between Great Britain and Finland.

Michael's home in London is 3 hours behind Erica's home in Rovaniemi.

It takes 3 hours to fly from London to Rovaniemi.

If Michael's plane leaves London at 10am what will the
time be in Rovaniemi when his plane touches down?

(Remember to state AM or PM)

4pm

You are at the end of the test. If you have time, go back and check your work.   4

22 / 30

Good work   73% 30

Time Started :

11+ Mathematics - Paper 8.

You have 35 minutes to complete this paper.

Q 1.

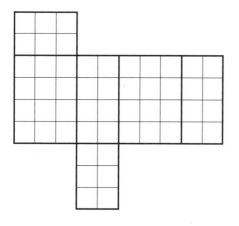

Look at the net on the left.
When folded it makes a box.

If the side of each small square is 1 cm,
what will be the total volume of the box?

_____ cm³

Q 2.   What is this number to 2 decimal places?

99.96582

_____

Q 3.   The product of 2 numbers is 45.

The difference between the two numbers is 4.

What are the two numbers?

_____ _____

Q 4.   What fraction of the months of the year have 30 days?

Write your answer in its lowest possible terms

_____

Q 5.   Which of these shapes has the shortest perimeter?   Circle the appropriate letter.

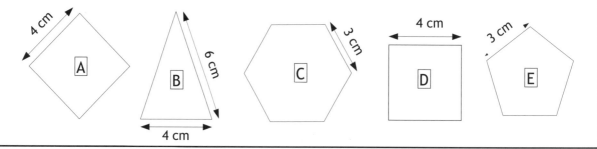

Q 6.   Find the missing number so that the equation balances.

8 x (3 + 4) = (8 + 6) x _____

6

Q 7—8.   Natasha and Christopher went to the local shop to buy some balloons for a party.
In the shop there were 5 different packs at 5 different prices:

A.	Gold & Silver Special	£3.65 / pack of 10
B.	Red & Green Jumbo	£3.20 / pack of 16
C.	Multicoloured Sausage	£2.20 / pack of 20
D.	Curly Whirly	£2.50 / pack of 25
E.	Small Red and Blue	£2.40 / pack of 12

Q 7.   What is the range of the prices of the packs?   _____

Q 8.   Which pack contains the balloons at the lowest price each?   _____

Q 9.   The ratio of flour to sugar in a cake is 6 : 5.

If a 660g mixture of flour and sugar was used to make the cake,
how much of it was flour?   _____ g

Q 10.

4.5 m

4 m

2 m

This is a floor plan of the twins' bedroom.

What is the perimeter of the room?   _____

Q 11.   Cooking oil can be bought in plastic bottles, small, medium and large.
If 2 large bottles hold as much as 3 medium bottles, which of the following statements
MUST be true? Tick the appropriate box.

A.	10 large bottles hold as much as 15 medium bottles.	☐
B.	Small bottles hold 1 litre.	☐
C.	12 medium bottles hold as much as 6 large.	☐
D.	8 large bottles hold as much as 16 medium bottles.	☐
E.	Large bottles hold 3 litres.	☐

5

Q 12. Which of the following numbers has a value closest to 100? Circle the appropriate answer.

99.951   99.929   100.099   99.099   100.899

Q 13. A box contains 2 red pens, 5 green pens and 3 blue pens.

If I pick a pen from the box at random (with my eyes shut), what is the probability that I will pick out a green one?   Circle the appropriate answer.

A. ½   B. 5/7   C. ⅕   D. ⅓   E. ⅖

Q 14. Scott's dad takes Scott and his three friends to a football match for a treat. It costs £14.00 for adults and £8.00 each for children. Each child also bought a programme and Scott's dad had a cup of coffee. Programmes are £2.20 each and cups of coffee cost £1.60.

How much does it cost Scott's dad altogether?   £ _____

Q 15. Which one of the numbers below includes 3, 5 and 9 as its factors?
Circle the appropriate answer.

9,   15,   27,   35,   45

Q 16. Look at the diagram below. Angle A is 120°.

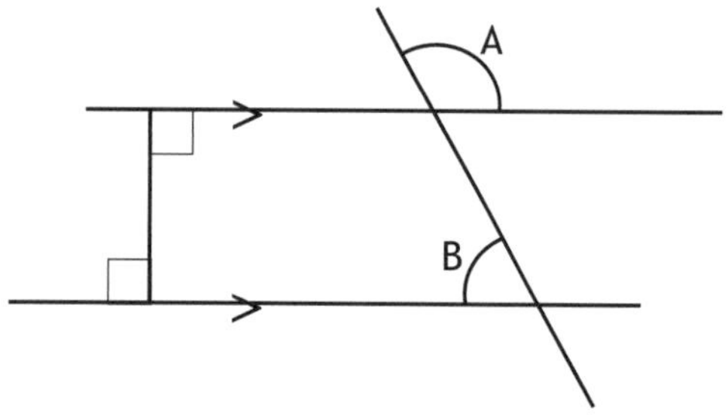

What is the angle B ?   _____°

Q 17. Joseph has two 50 pence pieces, two 20 pence pieces, a 10 pence piece and five 5 pence pieces in his pocket.

How much money does he have in total?   £ _____

Q 18. Caramel Fudge costs 58p per packet.
Jean bought 6 packets for herself and her friends.

How much change would Jean get from a £10 note?   £ _____

7

Q 19. Philippa adds her age to her sister Sonia's age. Between them they are half the age of their uncle Roy. Philippa is 4 years older than Sonia. Uncle Roy is 32.

How old is Phillipa? _____

Q 20.

Look at the shape on the left

The area of the shaded part is 132 cm².

What is the area of the whole shape? _____ cm²

Q 21. Mrs Edwards decorates wedding cakes for a local bakery.
She decorates 7 cakes every week, except when on holiday.
She takes 7 weeks holiday per year.

How many cakes does she decorate for the bakery in one year? _____ cakes

Q 22. Which of the following number is NOT a square number? Place a circle around the appropriate number.

36　　49　　66　　81　　144

Q 23. There are 462 people at a football match between
Braughton Rovers and Ofsted United.
There are 179 Ofsted fans in the ground.
The remainder support Broughton.

How many of the people in the ground support Braughton Rovers? _____

Q 24.

The hands of the classroom clock show the time 1 o'clock.

What will the size of acute angle be
between the hour hand and the minute hand? _____ °

Q 25. Which one of the following shapes will NOT form a letter when reflected in the line A B?
Circle the appropriate answer.

A ⁙⁙⁙⁙⁙⁙⁙⁙⁙⁙⁙⁙⁙⁙⁙⁙⁙⁙⁙⁙⁙⁙⁙⁙⁙⁙⁙⁙⁙ B

A	B	C	D	E

7

Q 26. This half term Kirsty has taken 7 mental maths tests. Here are her results out of 20:

17 13 18 15 14 18 16

What was her Median score? _____

Q 27.

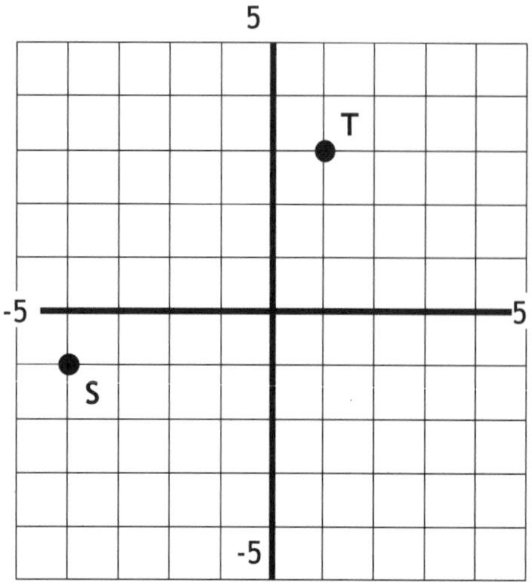

Look at the graph to the left.

Find the co-ordinates of **S** and **T**.

Place a cross in the appropriate box.

	S	T	
A.	(-1, 4)	(3, 1)	☐
B.	(-4, -1)	(1, 3)	☐
C.	(4, 1)	(3, 1)	☐
D.	(-4, -1)	(-1, 3)	☐
E.	(1, -4)	(-3, 1)	☐

Q 28. Grandpa still talks about measuring things in feet and inches.

Approximately how many centimetres are there in 1 foot? Circle the appropriate answer.

5 cm   15 cm   30 cm   50 cm   75 cm

Q 29.

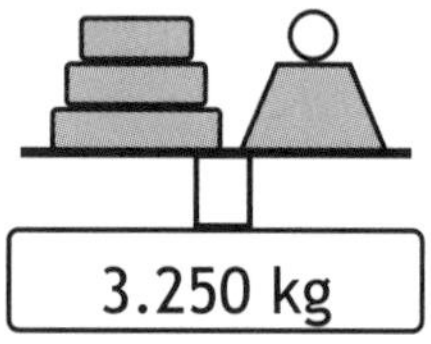

3.250 kg

John places some weights on an electronic scale. He needs to make a total of 3.7 kg.

Which two of the weights below should he choose to make up the weight to the correct amount?

Circle the two appropriate letters.

325g	150g	225g	275g	175g
A	B	C	D	E

Q 30. Sandra spends **x** pounds each week on magazines. She spends **y** pounds each month on make-up.

How much does Sandra spend altogether in a year? Place a cross in the appropriate box.

A. $52y + 12x$ ☐

B. $4x + 12y$ ☐

C. $12y \times 12x$ ☐

D. $52x + 10y$ ☐

E. $52x + 12y$ ☐

You are at the end of the test. If you have time, go back and check your work.

Time completed

11+ Mathematics - Paper 9.

You have 35 minutes to complete this paper.

Q 1. Mr and Mrs Johnson take their three children to the cinema.
It normally costs £5.50 for adults and £3.50 for children.
They buy a family ticket which costs £16.00.

How much do they save?   £ _____

Q 2.

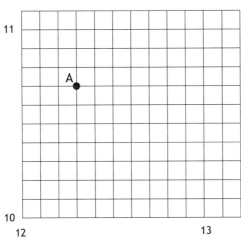

Look at this grid carefully.

What are the co-ordinates of point A?   (____ , ____)

Q 3. This is Colin's function machine.

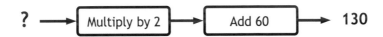

? ⟶ | Multiply by 2 | ⟶ | Add 60 | ⟶ **130**

What number did he start with?   _____

Q 4.

63	81	99
81	99	117
99	117	?

There is a number missing on this grid. What is it?   _____

Q 5. Baked beans are packed 36 tins to a box.
How many boxes would be needed to pack 756 tins?

_____

5

Q 6. Which of the following has the greatest value?   Circle the appropriate letter.

A ⅛ of 240   B 0.2 x 140   C ¼ of 160   D 35   E 30% of 120

Q 7. Which <u>two</u> of these nets will <u>NOT</u> fold to form a cube? Circle the appropriate letters.

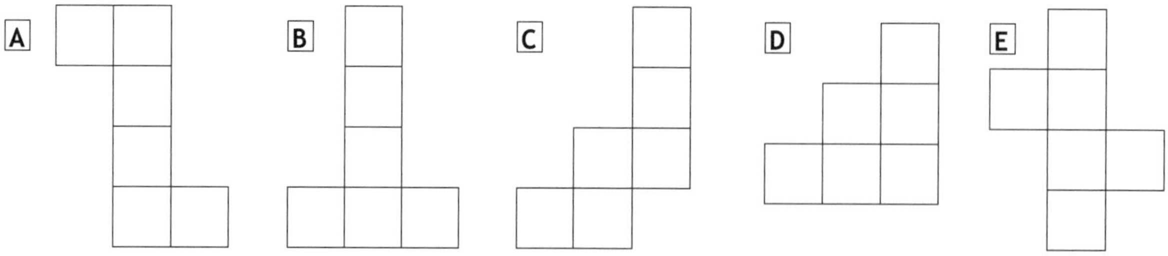

A   B   C   D   E

Q 8. Colin receives 25p pocket money per day.
If he saves all of it how much money will he have saved after 7 weeks?

£ _____

Q 9 - 11. This graph shows the number of fan letters delivered to the pop group **"Tone-deaf"** over a five week period.

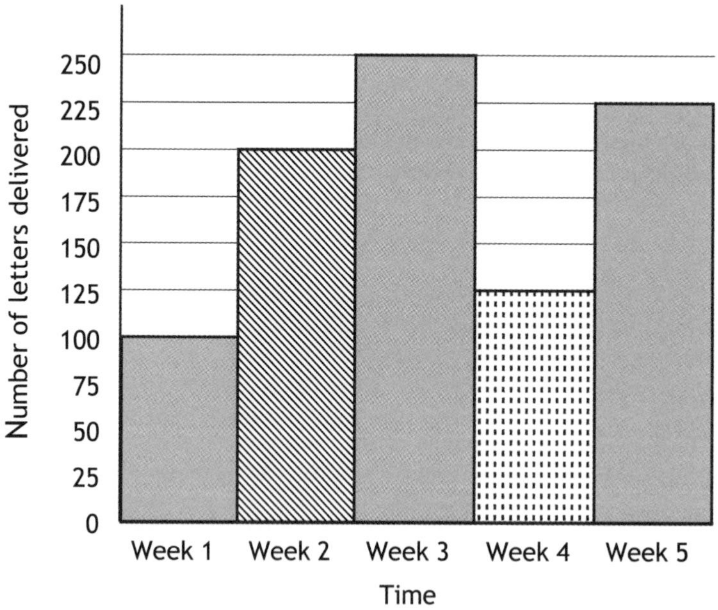

Q 9. What is the range of the numbers of letters received?   _____

Q 10. How many more fan letters were received in week 5 than in week 4?   _____

Q 11. In which <u>two</u> weeks did the band receive 425 fan letters altogether?

_____ , _____

Q 12. Catherine and Alex go to the Holiday Club each weekday morning during the summer. They have to pay £1.60 a day each to attend. Alex pays an extra 40p a day for a drink, whilst Catherine takes her own.

How much will it cost the pair of them to go to Holiday Club for one week? £ _____

Q 13. What fraction of an hour is 60 seconds?

Write your answer in its lowest possible terms. _____

Q 14. Jean's age is 4 years less than her brother Peter's was 3 years ago. Jane is now 7 years old.

How old is Peter? _____

Q 15.

Which of the above shapes has two sets of parallel sides, but no lines of symmetry?

Circle the appropriate letter.

Q 16.

10.2   10.3   10.4

What is the value of the number that the arrow is pointing towards? _____

Q 17. 480 athletes take part in a marathon.
⅝ complete the course in under 3 hours.

How many athletes took more than three hours? _____

Q 18. The florist sells large bunches of daffodils.
There are 18 daffodils in every large bunch.

How many bunches can the florist make from 864 daffodils? _____

7

Q 19-20. Mrs Campbell's class did a survey in their school on favourite television programmes.

Favourite T.V. Programmes	
Key: ☐ stands for 8 children ■ stands for 4 children	
Cartoon Time	☐■
Pop Chart Show	☐☐☐
Animal Capers	☐☐☐☐☐■
Battling Robots	☐☐■
Hospital Soap	☐☐☐☐

Q 19. How many children like the Animal Capers show? _____

Q 20. How many more children like the Pop Chart Show than Battling Robots? _____

Q 21. Stephanie has a bag which contains 11 normal spotted dice.

How many spots are there altogether? _____

Q 22. Mary, Theresa. June and Jessica all stood for election to the school council.

Theresa

Mary
25%

June
15%

Jessica
25%

300 children in the school voted for which girl they wanted to be their representative on the council.

How many votes did Theresa receive? _____

Q 23. The perimeter of a square is 16 cm. Two of these squares are placed side by side to form a rectangle.

What is the perimeter of the new rectangle? _____ cm

Q 24. Mr Erickson orders milk from the milkman 5 days a week. Each day he orders twice as much as the day before.

If he orders 2 litres on Monday, how many litres does he order on Friday? _____ litres

Q 25.   How many eggs would you have if you had 32 dozen?

_____   ☐

Q 26.   This is a map of the tunnels under Morton Castle. You must try to find your way from the <u>dining room</u> to the <u>lounge</u> using a set of instructions.

Key to the instructions:

FD means forward, **RT** means turn right 90° and **LT** means turn left 90°.

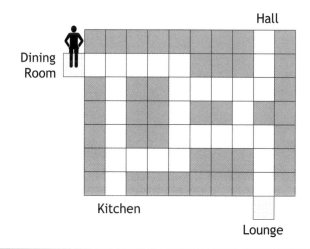

Which of these sets of instructions is the correct one? <u>Circle the appropriate letter.</u>

A   FD 5, RT, FD 4, LT, FD 4, RT, FD 3.

B.   FD 2, RT, FD 6, LT, FD 3, RT, FD 5.

C.   FD 2, LT, FD 3, RT, FD 5, RT, FD 3.

D.   FD 5, RT, FD 3, LT, FD 4, RT, FD 3.

E.   FD 5, RT, FD 3, LT, FD 5, RT, FD 3.

☐

Q 27.   How should 8.30 in the morning be written in the 24 hour clock?   _____   ☐

Q 28.   What fraction of 2 kilometres is 250 metres?

Write your answer in its lowest possible terms.   _____   ☐

Q 29.

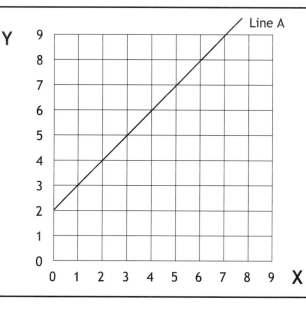

What is the rule that governs the plotting of line A?

<u>Circle the appropriate letter.</u>

A.   X = Y + 2

B.   Y = X - 2

C.   X = Y - 2

D.   Y = 2X

E.   2X = 2Y - 3

☐

Q 30.   Which one of the following numbers includes 3, 6 and 8 as its factors? Circle the appropriate answer.

18,   16,   36,   24,   28

☐

You are at the end of the test. If you have time, go back and check your work.   6

30

11+ Mathematics - Paper 10.

You have 35 minutes to complete this paper.

Q 1. Simon goes to a cinema club once every month.
He pays £2.30 each time he goes.

How much does he pay in one year?   £ _____

Q 2.

A — 6cm, 4cm

B — 2cm, 8cm

C — 3cm, 7cm

D — 5cm, 5cm

E — 1cm, 9cm

These shapes have the same perimeter, but which one has the largest area? _____

Q 3. Mr Edwards produced 738 tomatoes from
the tomato plants in his greenhouse. Each
plant grew an average of 18 tomatoes.

How many plants did he have in his greenhouse? _____

Q 4.

75	89	103
89	103	117
103	117	

There is a number missing on this grid. What is it? _____

Q 5. A class of 32 pupils were asked if they preferred tea, coffee or milk.
⅜ said they preferred coffee. ½ said they preferred tea.

How many children preferred milk? _____

Q 6. Tom, Barbara, Margot, Jerry and Colin each bought a shirt from the local market.
Tom paid £7.50, Margot £6.50, Barbara £9.00, Jerry £12.00 and Colin £11.95.
What was the range of amounts paid?   £_____

Q 7. Which of these sets of numbers contains all square numbers?

A.	16	39	54	☐
B.	25	49	72	☐
C.	39	64	81	☐ Place a cross in the appropriate box
D.	36	49	121	☐
E.	81	99	144	☐

Q 8. Which of these shapes has a rotational symmetry of order 2?

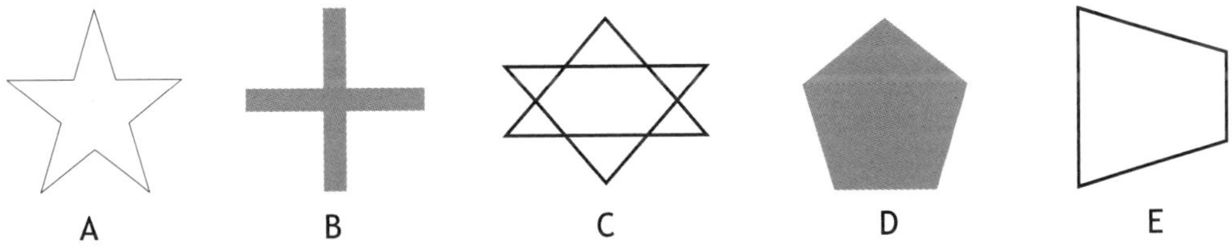

A   B   C   D   E

Q 9 - 11. This graph shows the number of chocolate bars sold by the school tuck shop in a five week period.

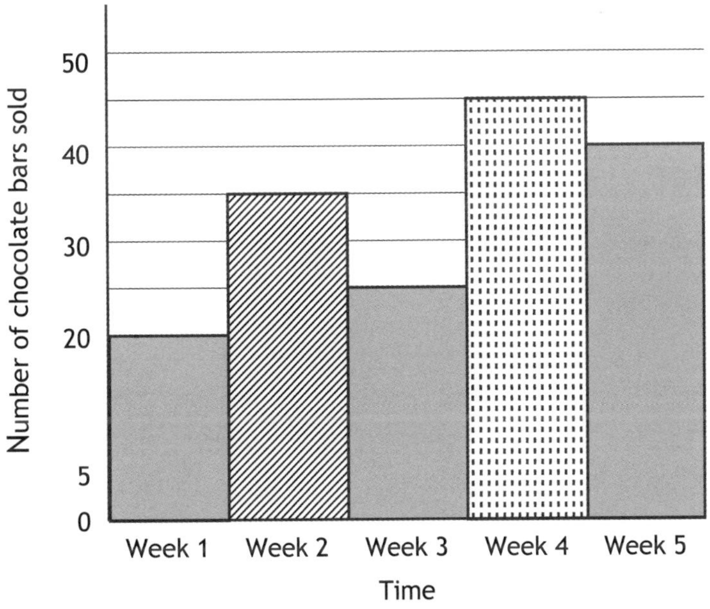

Q 9. What was the mean number of chocolate bars sold each week during the period?   _____

Q 10. How many more chocolate bars were sold in week 4 than in week 1?   _____

Q 11. Which two weeks had total sales of 55 chocolate bars?   Week _____ and week _____

6

Q 12.   There are 14 small sausages in a pack.

How many packs could you make from 98 sausages?   _____ packs

Q 13.   The local toy shop has a super sale.
Every item in the shop is reduced by 25%.
Charlie buys the radio controlled boat that he wants.
It normally costs £60.00.

How much does Charlie have to pay for the boat in the sale?   £ _____

Q 14.   In the same toyshop Charlie's sister, Mary,
bought a doll for £12.00.

What was the price of the doll BEFORE the sale started?   £ _____

Q 15.   This diagram shows part of a shape. It shows two of its lines of symmetry.

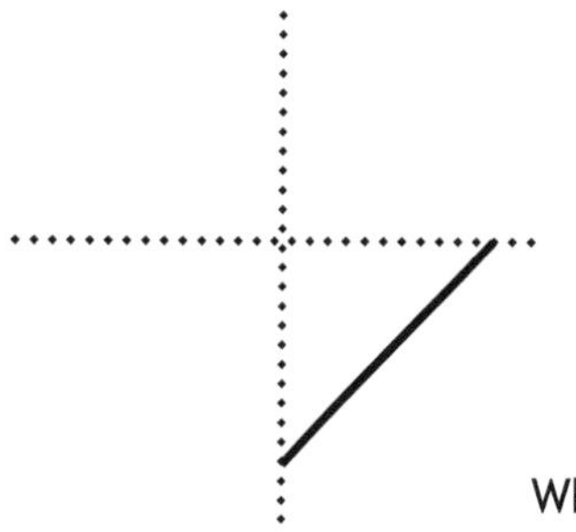

What is the name of the whole shape?   _____

Q 16 - 17.

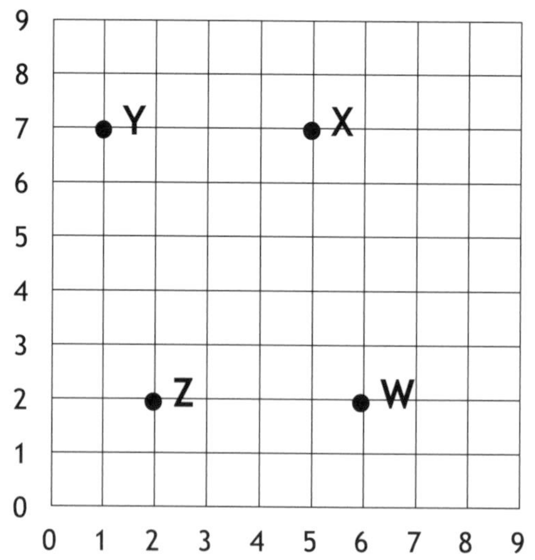

Q 16.   What are the co-ordinates of the points at letter W and letter Y?   W ____ , ____

Y ____ , ____

Q 17.   If you joined the points in alphabetical order, then back to W,
what shape would you have drawn?   _____

Q 18. Which of the figures below shows the number *fourteen thousand and forty*.

A. 14014 ☐
B. 140040 ☐
C. 14400 ☐   Place a cross in the appropriate box
D. 14040 ☐
E. 140440 ☐

☐

Q 19. What fraction of a day is 4 hours? _____

☐

Q 20. If $6y + 13 = 61$, then what is the value of y?

y = _____

☐

Q 21. There are 32 children in a class. 20 girls and 12 boys.
One child's name is chosen at random to take the register to the school office.

What is the chance that the child will be a girl?
(Show your answer as a fraction in its lowest terms.) _____

☐

Q 22. Sam's mum buys a 2 litre bottle of cola from the supermarket.
Approximately how much does it weigh?

(Write your answer in either kilos OR grams) _____

☐

Q 23. What is the total surface area of a cube with sides of 3 cm?

_____ cm²

☐

Q 24. Three corners of a square have the co-ordinates (2,9) (2,2) and (9,2).

What are the co-ordinates of the fourth corner? (_____ , _____)

☐

Q 25. Look at the two shapes below.
How many of the smaller shapes will fit EXACTLY into the larger shape?

1cm ↕ ◣   2cm ↕ ⬡

_____

☐

8

Q 26. In a nursery, there 648 boxes of plants.
139 are sold to the local council for a big flower display.
278 are sold to members of the public.

How many boxes remain unsold? _____

Q 27. Jane's mother is 3 times as old as Jane was 2 years ago.

If Jane's mum is 42, how old is Jane? _____

Q 28.

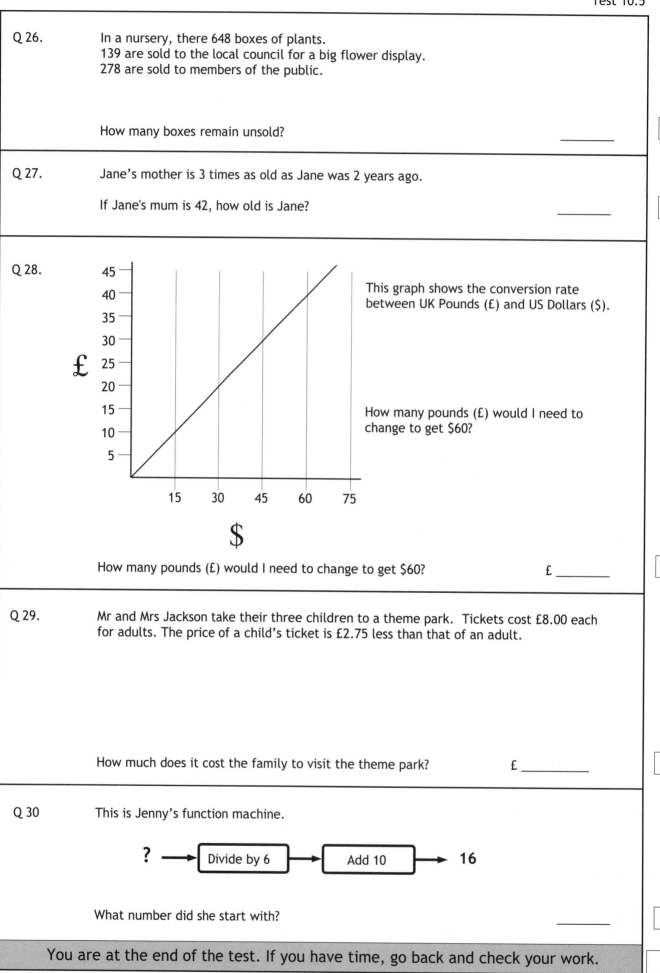

This graph shows the conversion rate between UK Pounds (£) and US Dollars ($).

How many pounds (£) would I need to change to get $60?

How many pounds (£) would I need to change to get $60? £ _____

Q 29. Mr and Mrs Jackson take their three children to a theme park. Tickets cost £8.00 each for adults. The price of a child's ticket is £2.75 less than that of an adult.

How much does it cost the family to visit the theme park? £ _____

Q 30 This is Jenny's function machine.

? ➔ Divide by 6 ➔ Add 10 ➔ 16

What number did she start with? _____

You are at the end of the test. If you have time, go back and check your work.

Mathematics Paper 1.   Answer Sheet

1.

A	[ ]
B	[ ]
C	[ ]
D	[ ]
E	[ ]

2.

A	[ ]
B	[ ]
C	[ ]
D	[ ]
E	[ ]

3.

A	[ ]
B	[ ]
C	[ ]
D	[ ]
E	[ ]

4.

16	[ ]
12	[ ]
15	[ ]
14	[ ]
13	[ ]

5.

60 cm²	[ ]
40 cm²	[ ]
76 cm²	[ ]
80 cm²	[ ]
120 cm²	[ ]

6.

4.15 pm	[ ]
4.35 am	[ ]
4.30 pm	[ ]
4.20 pm	[ ]
4.15 am	[ ]

7.

15	[ ]
17	[ ]
13	[ ]
14	[ ]
16	[ ]

8.

10	[ ]
9	[ ]
6	[ ]
7	[ ]
8	[ ]

9.

11.30 pm	[ ]
08.30 am	[ ]
23.30	[ ]
11.30	[ ]
23.30 am	[ ]

10.

10 cm²	[ ]
12 cm²	[ ]
20 cm²	[ ]
16 cm²	[ ]
24 cm²	[ ]

11.

A	[ ]
B	[ ]
C	[ ]
D	[ ]
E	[ ]

12.

0.909	[ ]
1.014	[ ]
0.97	[ ]
0.976	[ ]
1.011	[ ]

13.

2/5	[ ]
1/3	[ ]
1/2	[ ]
3/8	[ ]
4/10	[ ]

14.

150	[ ]
100	[ ]
60	[ ]
75	[ ]
120	[ ]

15.

255	[ ]
315	[ ]
275	[ ]
333	[ ]
225	[ ]

16.

40	[ ]
54	[ ]
47	[ ]
52	[ ]
45	[ ]

17.

45 cm	[ ]
30 cm	[ ]
35 cm	[ ]
25 cm	[ ]
40 cm	[ ]

18.

24	[ ]
27	[ ]
39	[ ]
43	[ ]
54	[ ]

19.

11	[ ]
15	[ ]
12	[ ]
14	[ ]
10	[ ]

20.

9.98	[ ]
9.807	[ ]
9.87	[ ]
9.907	[ ]
9.078	[ ]

21.

48	[ ]
60	[ ]
72	[ ]
56	[ ]
66	[ ]

22.

28	[ ]
14	[ ]
48	[ ]
42	[ ]
36	[ ]

23.

175	[ ]
250	[ ]
225	[ ]
200	[ ]
150	[ ]

24.

75	[ ]
100	[ ]
125	[ ]
50	[ ]
60	[ ]

25.

Week 1	[ ]
Week 2	[ ]
Week 3	[ ]
Week 4	[ ]
Week 5	[ ]

26.

56%	[ ]
54%	[ ]
46%	[ ]
52%	[ ]
44%	[ ]

27.

£32.60	[ ]
£33.20	[ ]
£32.80	[ ]
£32.40	[ ]
£34.20	[ ]

28.

A	[ ]
B	[ ]
C	[ ]
D	[ ]
E	[ ]

29.

11.06 Kg	[ ]
110.06 Kg	[ ]
1100.6 Kg	[ ]
11.006 Kg	[ ]
110.6 Kg	[ ]

30.

(18 , 13)	[ ]
(17 , 14)	[ ]
(14 , 18)	[ ]
(18 , 14)	[ ]
(13 , 18)	[ ]

Mathematics Paper 2.   Answer Sheet

1.

£94.00	[ ]
£52.00	[ ]
£65.00	[ ]
£70.00	[ ]
£78.00	[ ]

2.

234 cm²	[ ]
204 cm²	[ ]
314 cm²	[ ]
284 cm²	[ ]
243 cm²	[ ]

3.

A	[ ]
B	[ ]
C	[ ]
D	[ ]
E	[ ]

4.

15	[ ]
13	[ ]
16	[ ]
12	[ ]
14	[ ]

5.

32	[ ]
30	[ ]
22	[ ]
36	[ ]
20	[ ]

6.

£5.40	[ ]
£1.80	[ ]
£3.60	[ ]
£2.40	[ ]
£4.80	[ ]

7.

45	[ ]
52	[ ]
35	[ ]
28	[ ]
30	[ ]

8.

£2.40	[ ]
£1.40	[ ]
£1.60	[ ]
£1.80	[ ]
£2.60	[ ]

9.

28m	[ ]
32m	[ ]
36m	[ ]
34m	[ ]
72m	[ ]

10.

A	[ ]
B	[ ]
C	[ ]
D	[ ]
E	[ ]

11.

5.1439	[ ]
5.0967	[ ]
4.8759	[ ]
5.0899	[ ]
4.7499	[ ]

12.

7/12	[ ]
8/10	[ ]
3/4	[ ]
2/3	[ ]
4/5	[ ]

13.

17	[ ]
18	[ ]
14	[ ]
12	[ ]
13	[ ]

14.

£150.00	[ ]
£235.00	[ ]
£200.00	[ ]
£225.00	[ ]
£175.00	[ ]

15.

£160.00	[ ]
£175.00	[ ]
£150.00	[ ]
£145.00	[ ]
£155.00	[ ]

16.

16	[ ]
8	[ ]
12	[ ]
10	[ ]
6	[ ]

17.

X (7 , 7) , Z (3 , 2)	[ ]
X (5 , 7) , Z (3 , 2)	[ ]
X (3 , 2) , Z (7 , 5)	[ ]
X (7 , 7) , Z (2 , 3)	[ ]
X (3 , 2) , Z (7 , 5)	[ ]

18.

Kite	[ ]
Trapezium	[ ]
Rhombus	[ ]
Pentagon	[ ]
Rectangle	[ ]

19.

40°	[ ]
80°	[ ]
50°	[ ]
60°	[ ]
45°	[ ]

20.

£2.40	[ ]
£2.55	[ ]
£2.66	[ ]
£2.15	[ ]
£2.30	[ ]

21.

25	[ ]
49	[ ]
64	[ ]
110	[ ]
121	[ ]

22.

A	[ ]
B	[ ]
C	[ ]
D	[ ]
E	[ ]

23.

A	[ ]
B	[ ]
C	[ ]
D	[ ]
E	[ ]

24.

14	[ ]
17	[ ]
18	[ ]
16	[ ]
15	[ ]

25.

0.25	[ ]
0.025	[ ]
0.2005	[ ]
0.0025	[ ]
0.0205	[ ]

26.

124	[ ]
141	[ ]
138	[ ]
132	[ ]
137	[ ]

27.

13	[ ]
11	[ ]
12	[ ]
14	[ ]
8	[ ]

28.

Au$ 175.00	[ ]
Au$ 160.00	[ ]
Au$ 195.00	[ ]
Au$ 190.00	[ ]
Au$ 180.00	[ ]

29.

£27.50	[ ]
£28.00	[ ]
£29.25	[ ]
£27.00	[ ]
£35.50	[ ]

30.

70	[ ]
78	[ ]
18	[ ]
68	[ ]
24	[ ]

Mathematics Paper 3.   Answer Sheet

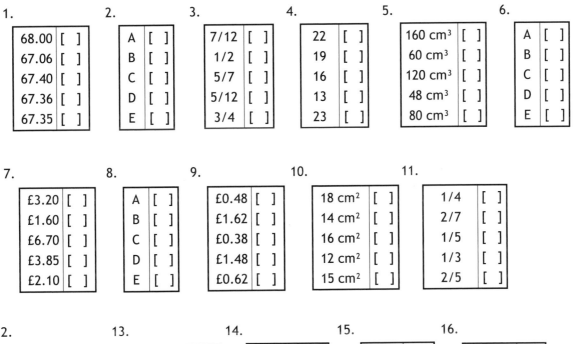

1.
68.00	[ ]
67.06	[ ]
67.40	[ ]
67.36	[ ]
67.35	[ ]

2.
A	[ ]
B	[ ]
C	[ ]
D	[ ]
E	[ ]

3.
7/12	[ ]
1/2	[ ]
5/7	[ ]
5/12	[ ]
3/4	[ ]

4.
22	[ ]
19	[ ]
16	[ ]
13	[ ]
23	[ ]

5.
160 cm³	[ ]
60 cm³	[ ]
120 cm³	[ ]
48 cm³	[ ]
80 cm³	[ ]

6.
A	[ ]
B	[ ]
C	[ ]
D	[ ]
E	[ ]

7.
£3.20	[ ]
£1.60	[ ]
£6.70	[ ]
£3.85	[ ]
£2.10	[ ]

8.
A	[ ]
B	[ ]
C	[ ]
D	[ ]
E	[ ]

9.
£0.48	[ ]
£1.62	[ ]
£0.38	[ ]
£1.48	[ ]
£0.62	[ ]

10.
18 cm²	[ ]
14 cm²	[ ]
16 cm²	[ ]
12 cm²	[ ]
15 cm²	[ ]

11.
1/4	[ ]
2/7	[ ]
1/5	[ ]
1/3	[ ]
2/5	[ ]

12.
9.0967	[ ]
10.1439	[ ]
9.8763	[ ]
9.7439	[ ]
10.0967	[ ]

13.
7/12	[ ]
3/5	[ ]
8/12	[ ]
3/10	[ ]
1/3	[ ]

14.
£21.40	[ ]
£20.10	[ ]
£18.60	[ ]
£22.00	[ ]
£23.40	[ ]

15.
1000g	[ ]
500g	[ ]
450g	[ ]
800g	[ ]
750g	[ ]

16.
13, 9	[ ]
14, 10	[ ]
12, 16	[ ]
11, 7	[ ]
12, 8	[ ]

17.
310 cm²	[ ]
224 cm²	[ ]
336 cm²	[ ]
350 cm²	[ ]
290 cm²	[ ]

18.
13	[ ]
12	[ ]
16	[ ]
15	[ ]
19	[ ]

19.
240°	[ ]
160°	[ ]
120°	[ ]
200°	[ ]
145°	[ ]

20.
60°	[ ]
160°	[ ]
100°	[ ]
120°	[ ]
145°	[ ]

21.
£2.35	[ ]
£1.65	[ ]
£1.85	[ ]
£2.05	[ ]
£2.55	[ ]

22.
36	[ ]
56	[ ]
81	[ ]
121	[ ]
169	[ ]

23.
Square	[ ]
Pentagon	[ ]
Hexagon	[ ]
Rhombus	[ ]
Trapezium	[ ]

24.
2y + 5x	[ ]
x + 7y	[ ]
5y + 2x	[ ]
7x + y	[ ]
7x + 7y	[ ]

25.
9	[ ]
17	[ ]
16	[ ]
5	[ ]
18	[ ]

26.
0.5l	[ ]
4.5l	[ ]
8.5l	[ ]
10l	[ ]
15l	[ ]

27.
A	[ ]
B	[ ]
C	[ ]
D	[ ]
E	[ ]

28.
A	[ ]
B	[ ]
C	[ ]
D	[ ]
E	[ ]

29.
A	[ ]
B	[ ]
C	[ ]
D	[ ]
E	[ ]

30.
1 pm	[ ]
2 am	[ ]
11 pm	[ ]
1 am	[ ]
3 am	[ ]

Mathematics Paper 4.   Answer Sheet

1.
£7.40	[ ]
£8.40	[ ]
£9.00	[ ]
£8.60	[ ]
£7.80	[ ]

2.
(14, 1.3)	[ ]
(13, 1.4)	[ ]
(1.4, 14)	[ ]
(13, 1.3)	[ ]
(1.3, 13)	[ ]

3.
13	[ ]
21	[ ]
15	[ ]
6	[ ]
9	[ ]

4.
A	[ ]
B	[ ]
C	[ ]
D	[ ]
E	[ ]

5.
A	[ ]
B	[ ]
C	[ ]
D	[ ]
E	[ ]

6.
19	[ ]
17	[ ]
18	[ ]
15	[ ]
12	[ ]

7.
39	[ ]
42	[ ]
38	[ ]
41	[ ]
40	[ ]

8.
40%	[ ]
45%	[ ]
48%	[ ]
38%	[ ]
50%	[ ]

9.
100 cm	[ ]
150 cm	[ ]
200 cm	[ ]
250 cm	[ ]
300 cm	[ ]

10.
£9.20	[ ]
£12.80	[ ]
£9.60	[ ]
£10.60	[ ]
£8.20	[ ]

11.
£8.20	[ ]
£8.80	[ ]
£10.50	[ ]
£12.50	[ ]
£6.80	[ ]

12.
16	[ ]
28	[ ]
32	[ ]
42	[ ]
45	[ ]

13.
24	[ ]
20	[ ]
18	[ ]
28	[ ]
30	[ ]

14.
72	[ ]
66	[ ]
56	[ ]
60	[ ]
80	[ ]

15.
50 cm²	[ ]
70 cm²	[ ]
100 cm²	[ ]
80 cm²	[ ]
144 cm²	[ ]

16.
50	[ ]
72	[ ]
60	[ ]
45	[ ]
55	[ ]

17.
35	[ ]
18	[ ]
25	[ ]
31	[ ]
27	[ ]

18.
100	[ ]
150	[ ]
90	[ ]
120	[ ]
140	[ ]

19.
1/3	[ ]
5/12	[ ]
2/5	[ ]
3/8	[ ]
1/4	[ ]

20.
26.5	[ ]
25.65	[ ]
26.45	[ ]
27.4	[ ]
26.6	[ ]

21.
120	[ ]
150	[ ]
135	[ ]
115	[ ]
130	[ ]

22.
27	[ ]
33	[ ]
30	[ ]
36	[ ]
21	[ ]

23.
10	[ ]
15	[ ]
12	[ ]
21	[ ]
18	[ ]

24.
30 cm	[ ]
42 cm	[ ]
48 cm	[ ]
36 cm	[ ]
38 cm	[ ]

25.
114	[ ]
120	[ ]
110	[ ]
96	[ ]
104	[ ]

26.
A	[ ]
B	[ ]
C	[ ]
D	[ ]
E	[ ]

27.
5.30 am	[ ]
7.30 pm	[ ]
6.30 am	[ ]
5.30 pm	[ ]
7.30 am	[ ]

28.
7	[ ]
6	[ ]
3	[ ]
5	[ ]
4	[ ]

30.
A	[ ]
B	[ ]
C	[ ]
D	[ ]
E	[ ]

30.
A	[ ]
B	[ ]
C	[ ]
D	[ ]
E	[ ]

Mathematics Paper 5.   Answer Sheet

1.
£90.60	[ ]
£86.50	[ ]
£88.40	[ ]
£93.60	[ ]
£97.40	[ ]

2.
A	[ ]
B	[ ]
C	[ ]
D	[ ]
E	[ ]

3.
£31.20	[ ]
£28.80	[ ]
£29.80	[ ]
£26.60	[ ]
£35.80	[ ]

4.
A	[ ]
B	[ ]
C	[ ]
D	[ ]
E	[ ]

5.
£3.95	[ ]
£9.45	[ ]
£4.35	[ ]
£5.65	[ ]
£6.35	[ ]

6.
155	[ ]
165	[ ]
150	[ ]
170	[ ]
160	[ ]

7.
120	[ ]
125	[ ]
150	[ ]
175	[ ]
160	[ ]

8.
Week 1	[ ]
Week 2	[ ]
Week 3	[ ]
Week 4	[ ]
Week 5	[ ]

9.
25	[ ]
22	[ ]
15	[ ]
20	[ ]
18	[ ]

10.
A	[ ]
B	[ ]
C	[ ]
D	[ ]
E	[ ]

11.
51	[ ]
48	[ ]
30	[ ]
52	[ ]
50	[ ]

12.
£14.00	[ ]
£13.50	[ ]
£12.00	[ ]
£16.50	[ ]
£10.80	[ ]

13.
£40.00	[ ]
£46.00	[ ]
£54.00	[ ]
£48.00	[ ]
£44.00	[ ]

14.
A	[ ]
B	[ ]
C	[ ]
D	[ ]
E	[ ]

15.
9	[ ]
18	[ ]
6	[ ]
8	[ ]
12	[ ]

16.
13/20	[ ]
7/10	[ ]
4/10	[ ]
7/20	[ ]
5/12	[ ]

17.
Hexagon	[ ]
Pentagon	[ ]
Rhombus	[ ]
Kite	[ ]
Octagon	[ ]

18.
1/2	[ ]
2/3	[ ]
1/3	[ ]
1/6	[ ]
2/5	[ ]

19.
6	[ ]
3	[ ]
1	[ ]
5	[ ]
4	[ ]

20.
W (3, 5) , Y (5, 1)	[ ]
W (5, 7) , Y (3, 5)	[ ]
W (7, 3) , Y (5, 7)	[ ]
W (5, 7) , Y (5, 3)	[ ]
W (7, 5) , Y (3, 5)	[ ]

21.
Pentagon	[ ]
Trapezium	[ ]
Rhombus	[ ]
Kite	[ ]
Rectangle	[ ]

22.
A	[ ]
B	[ ]
C	[ ]
D	[ ]
E	[ ]

23.
64 cm³	[ ]
56 cm³	[ ]
40 cm³	[ ]
32 cm³	[ ]
80 cm³	[ ]

24.
58	[ ]
60	[ ]
44	[ ]
52	[ ]
38	[ ]

25.
(2, 7)	[ ]
(1, 7)	[ ]
(7, 1)	[ ]
(8, 2)	[ ]
(8, 1)	[ ]

26.
Au$ 75.00	[ ]
Au$ 60.00	[ ]
Au$ 95.00	[ ]
Au$ 90.00	[ ]
Au$ 85.00	[ ]

27.
529	[ ]
559	[ ]
531	[ ]
549	[ ]
551	[ ]

28.
13	[ ]
11	[ ]
12	[ ]
9	[ ]
10	[ ]

29.
6	[ ]
10	[ ]
12	[ ]
9	[ ]
8	[ ]

30.
36	[ ]
28	[ ]
40	[ ]
34	[ ]
42	[ ]

Mathematics Paper 6.   Answer Sheet

1.

£12.00	[ ]
£14.60	[ ]
£15.80	[ ]
£16.00	[ ]
£14.00	[ ]

2.

75 cm²	[ ]
100 cm²	[ ]
90 cm²	[ ]
120 cm²	[ ]
56 cm²	[ ]

3.

A	[ ]
B	[ ]
C	[ ]
D	[ ]
E	[ ]

4.

25	[ ]
18	[ ]
24	[ ]
23	[ ]
27	[ ]

5.

15	[ ]
19	[ ]
16	[ ]
14	[ ]
13	[ ]

6.

151	[ ]
155	[ ]
161	[ ]
145	[ ]
165	[ ]

7.

11	[ ]
9	[ ]
12	[ ]
14	[ ]
13	[ ]

8.

60°	[ ]
120°	[ ]
80°	[ ]
45°	[ ]
100°	[ ]

9.

£54.00	[ ]
£44.50	[ ]
£40.50	[ ]
£38.00	[ ]
£56.50	[ ]

10.

63	[ ]
72	[ ]
56	[ ]
81	[ ]
69	[ ]

11.

1/6	[ ]
2/3	[ ]
3/4	[ ]
1/3	[ ]
2/6	[ ]

12.

165°	[ ]
120°	[ ]
150°	[ ]
145°	[ ]
100°	[ ]

13.

£3.05	[ ]
£3.15	[ ]
£3.45	[ ]
£2.95	[ ]
£3.35	[ ]

14.

30	[ ]
40	[ ]
50	[ ]
70	[ ]
80	[ ]

15.

A	[ ]
B	[ ]
C	[ ]
D	[ ]
E	[ ]

16.

A	[ ]
B	[ ]
C	[ ]
D	[ ]
E	[ ]

17.

11	[ ]
14	[ ]
15	[ ]
13	[ ]
12	[ ]

18.

1.270	[ ]
0.127	[ ]
12.70	[ ]
1.027	[ ]
0.0127	[ ]

19.

5/8	[ ]
6/10	[ ]
2/3	[ ]
3/5	[ ]
3/10	[ ]

20.

80m	[ ]
48m	[ ]
78m	[ ]
136m	[ ]
68m	[ ]

21.

480g	[ ]
520g	[ ]
400g	[ ]
360g	[ ]
380g	[ ]

22.

14	[ ]
8	[ ]
9	[ ]
13	[ ]
12	[ ]

23.

12	[ ]
13	[ ]
9	[ ]
8	[ ]
11	[ ]

24.

£0.74	[ ]
£1.13	[ ]
£0.96	[ ]
£0.84	[ ]
£0.98	[ ]

25.

28	[ ]
27	[ ]
22	[ ]
24	[ ]
26	[ ]

26.

£14.00	[ ]
£21.50	[ ]
£18.00	[ ]
£16.00	[ ]
£15.00	[ ]

27.

£9.00	[ ]
£15.00	[ ]
£11.00	[ ]
£12.50	[ ]
£10.00	[ ]

28.

8	[ ]
6	[ ]
4	[ ]
5	[ ]
7	[ ]

29.

F (2 , 4) H (7 , 8)	[ ]
F (8 , 7) H (4 , 2)	[ ]
F (2 , 4) H (8 , 7)	[ ]
F (4 , 2) H (8 , 7)	[ ]
F (7 , 8) H (4 , 2)	[ ]

30.

Rhombus	[ ]
Pentagon	[ ]
Parallelogram	[ ]
Kite	[ ]
Trapezium	[ ]

Mathematics Paper 7.   Answer Sheet

1.

147.00	[ ]
146.56	[ ]
146.60	[ ]
147.60	[ ]
146.55	[ ]

2.

75 cm²	[ ]
45 cm²	[ ]
50 cm²	[ ]
60 cm²	[ ]
55 cm²	[ ]

3.

4/5	[ ]
4/10	[ ]
1/3	[ ]
3/8	[ ]
2/5	[ ]

4.

15	[ ]
14	[ ]
16	[ ]
13	[ ]
19	[ ]

5.

75 cm²	[ ]
64 cm²	[ ]
104 cm²	[ ]
52 cm²	[ ]
208 cm²	[ ]

6.

A	[ ]
B	[ ]
C	[ ]
D	[ ]
E	[ ]

7.

£7.03	[ ]
£2.48	[ ]
£3.68	[ ]
£1.98	[ ]
£1.64	[ ]

8.

A	[ ]
B	[ ]
C	[ ]
D	[ ]
E	[ ]

9.

A	[ ]
B	[ ]
C	[ ]
D	[ ]
E	[ ]

10.

31	[ ]
29	[ ]
30	[ ]
25	[ ]
27	[ ]

11.

20	[ ]
25	[ ]
30	[ ]
15	[ ]
22	[ ]

12.

Simon	[ ]
Denise	[ ]
Jenny	[ ]
Sonia	[ ]
Habib	[ ]

13.

1/2	[ ]
1/3	[ ]
2/3	[ ]
1/6	[ ]
5/6	[ ]

14.

350g	[ ]
450g	[ ]
750g	[ ]
280g	[ ]
250g	[ ]

15.

35, 2	[ ]
10, 7	[ ]
34, 36	[ ]
37, 33	[ ]
3, 25	[ ]

16.

64 cm²	[ ]
54 cm²	[ ]
63 cm²	[ ]
72 cm²	[ ]
74 cm²	[ ]

17.

34	[ ]
36	[ ]
39	[ ]
37	[ ]
40	[ ]

18.

120°	[ ]
60°	[ ]
45°	[ ]
75°	[ ]
90°	[ ]

19.

A	[ ]
B	[ ]
C	[ ]
D	[ ]
E	[ ]

20.

90°	[ ]
80°	[ ]
45°	[ ]
60°	[ ]
30°	[ ]

21.

7	[ ]
10	[ ]
8	[ ]
6	[ ]
9	[ ]

22.

9/16	[ ]
4/12	[ ]
5/8	[ ]
5/12	[ ]
9/24	[ ]

23.

6 kg	[ ]
500g	[ ]
2.5 kg	[ ]
4000g	[ ]
15 kg	[ ]

24.

50 cm³	[ ]
15 cm³	[ ]
125 cm³	[ ]
75 cm³	[ ]
100 cm³	[ ]

25.

0.65	[ ]
65.0	[ ]
0.065	[ ]
0.605	[ ]
0.0065	[ ]

26.

10	[ ]
8	[ ]
6	[ ]
12	[ ]
9	[ ]

27.

5	[ ]
2	[ ]
4	[ ]
2.5	[ ]
3	[ ]

28.

A	[ ]
B	[ ]
C	[ ]
D	[ ]
E	[ ]

29.

A	[ ]
B	[ ]
C	[ ]
D	[ ]
E	[ ]

30.

10 am	[ ]
1 pm	[ ]
4 pm	[ ]
1 am	[ ]
3 pm	[ ]

Mathematics Paper 8.   Answer Sheet

1.

36 cm³	[ ]
24 cm³	[ ]
16 cm³	[ ]
48 cm³	[ ]
32 cm³	[ ]

2.

100.00	[ ]
99.96	[ ]
99.90	[ ]
99.97	[ ]
100.06	[ ]

3.

10, 6	[ ]
11, 7	[ ]
5, 8	[ ]
8, 4	[ ]
9, 5	[ ]

4.

3/12	[ ]
1/3	[ ]
1/4	[ ]
1/6	[ ]
5/12	[ ]

5.

A	[ ]
B	[ ]
C	[ ]
D	[ ]
E	[ ]

6.

6	[ ]
5	[ ]
7	[ ]
4	[ ]
3	[ ]

7.

£1.90	[ ]
£1.45	[ ]
£1.70	[ ]
£2.05	[ ]
£1.85	[ ]

8.

A	[ ]
B	[ ]
C	[ ]
D	[ ]
E	[ ]

9.

420g	[ ]
360g	[ ]
300g	[ ]
450g	[ ]
520g	[ ]

10.

25m	[ ]
19m	[ ]
22m	[ ]
24m	[ ]
17m	[ ]

11.

A	[ ]
B	[ ]
C	[ ]
D	[ ]
E	[ ]

12.

99.951	[ ]
99.929	[ ]
100.099	[ ]
99.099	[ ]
100.899	[ ]

13.

A	[ ]
B	[ ]
C	[ ]
D	[ ]
E	[ ]

14.

£52.40	[ ]
£48.80	[ ]
£46.60	[ ]
£60.00	[ ]
£56.40	[ ]

15.

9	[ ]
15	[ ]
27	[ ]
35	[ ]
45	[ ]

16.

60°	[ ]
80°	[ ]
75°	[ ]
45°	[ ]
100°	[ ]

17.

£1.90	[ ]
£1.75	[ ]
£1.70	[ ]
£2.25	[ ]
£1.35	[ ]

18.

£6.74	[ ]
£6.42	[ ]
£6.48	[ ]
£6.32	[ ]
£6.52	[ ]

19.

9	[ ]
11	[ ]
12	[ ]
7	[ ]
10	[ ]

20.

320 cm²	[ ]
264 cm²	[ ]
396 cm²	[ ]
290 cm²	[ ]
334 cm²	[ ]

21.

355	[ ]
315	[ ]
305	[ ]
300	[ ]
295	[ ]

22.

36	[ ]
49	[ ]
66	[ ]
81	[ ]
144	[ ]

23.

283	[ ]
273	[ ]
293	[ ]
271	[ ]
291	[ ]

24.

45°	[ ]
20°	[ ]
15°	[ ]
30°	[ ]
25°	[ ]

25.

A	[ ]
B	[ ]
C	[ ]
D	[ ]
E	[ ]

26.

14	[ ]
17	[ ]
16	[ ]
15	[ ]
18	[ ]

27.

A	[ ]
B	[ ]
C	[ ]
D	[ ]
E	[ ]

28.

5 cm	[ ]
10 cm	[ ]
30 cm	[ ]
50 cm	[ ]
75 cm	[ ]

29.

A	[ ]
B	[ ]
C	[ ]
D	[ ]
E	[ ]

30.

A	[ ]
B	[ ]
C	[ ]
D	[ ]
E	[ ]

Mathematics Paper 9.   Answer Sheet

1.
£6.50	[ ]
£5.00	[ ]
£6.75	[ ]
£5.50	[ ]
£4.75	[ ]

2.
(12.6) (10.7)	[ ]
(12.6) (17.0)	[ ]
(12.3) (10.7)	[ ]
(12.6) (11.6)	[ ]
(12.3) (17.6)	[ ]

3.
50	[ ]
45	[ ]
95	[ ]
35	[ ]
140	[ ]

4.
130	[ ]
129	[ ]
123	[ ]
135	[ ]
133	[ ]

5.
19	[ ]
17	[ ]
23	[ ]
18	[ ]
21	[ ]

6.
A	[ ]
B	[ ]
C	[ ]
D	[ ]
E	[ ]

7.
A	[ ]
B	[ ]
C	[ ]
D	[ ]
E	[ ]

8.
£12.50	[ ]
£12.25	[ ]
£11.75	[ ]
£3.50	[ ]
£1.75	[ ]

9.
125	[ ]
115	[ ]
100	[ ]
135	[ ]
150	[ ]

10.
125	[ ]
100	[ ]
225	[ ]
175	[ ]
150	[ ]

11.
Week 1	[ ]
Week 2	[ ]
Week 3	[ ]
Week 4	[ ]
Week 5	[ ]

12.
£20.00	[ ]
£15.00	[ ]
£18.00	[ ]
£17.50	[ ]
£18.50	[ ]

13.
5/60	[ ]
1/4	[ ]
6/10	[ ]
1/50	[ ]
1/60	[ ]

14.
11	[ ]
16	[ ]
15	[ ]
17	[ ]
14	[ ]

15.
A	[ ]
B	[ ]
C	[ ]
D	[ ]
E	[ ]

16.
10.70	[ ]
10.30	[ ]
10.35	[ ]
10.44	[ ]
10.36	[ ]

17.
180	[ ]
240	[ ]
160	[ ]
120	[ ]
200	[ ]

18.
36	[ ]
52	[ ]
54	[ ]
48	[ ]
56	[ ]

19.
44	[ ]
36	[ ]
28	[ ]
41	[ ]
38	[ ]

20.
8	[ ]
4	[ ]
7	[ ]
6	[ ]
2	[ ]

21.
231	[ ]
245	[ ]
200	[ ]
256	[ ]
280	[ ]

22.
120	[ ]
60	[ ]
105	[ ]
95	[ ]
75	[ ]

23.
24 cm	[ ]
16 cm	[ ]
20 cm	[ ]
18 cm	[ ]
32 cm	[ ]

24.
10	[ ]
16	[ ]
30	[ ]
24	[ ]
32	[ ]

25.
348	[ ]
268	[ ]
628	[ ]
384	[ ]
624	[ ]

26.
A	[ ]
B	[ ]
C	[ ]
D	[ ]
E	[ ]

27.
08.30 pm	[ ]
08.30 am	[ ]
20.30	[ ]
8.30	[ ]
08.30	[ ]

28.
1/2	[ ]
5/8	[ ]
5/16	[ ]
1/8	[ ]
3/4	[ ]

29.
A	[ ]
B	[ ]
C	[ ]
D	[ ]
E	[ ]

30.
18	[ ]
16	[ ]
36	[ ]
24	[ ]
28	[ ]

Mathematics Paper 10.   Answer Sheet

1.

£28.40	[ ]
£26.50	[ ]
£27.60	[ ]
£27.00	[ ]
£25.60	[ ]

2.

A	[ ]
B	[ ]
C	[ ]
D	[ ]
E	[ ]

3.

27	[ ]
35	[ ]
60	[ ]
41	[ ]
29	[ ]

4.

129	[ ]
131	[ ]
128	[ ]
130	[ ]
124	[ ]

5.

3	[ ]
4	[ ]
6	[ ]
7	[ ]
8	[ ]

6.

£2.80	[ ]
£3.65	[ ]
£4.20	[ ]
£4.80	[ ]
£5.50	[ ]

7.

A	[ ]
B	[ ]
C	[ ]
D	[ ]
E	[ ]

8.

A	[ ]
B	[ ]
C	[ ]
D	[ ]
E	[ ]

9.

30	[ ]
41	[ ]
37	[ ]
33	[ ]
30	[ ]

10

25	[ ]
15	[ ]
20	[ ]
45	[ ]
30	[ ]

11.

1	[ ]
2	[ ]
3	[ ]
4	[ ]
5	[ ]

12.

11	[ ]
6	[ ]
8	[ ]
9	[ ]
7	[ ]

13.

£80.00	[ ]
£50.00	[ ]
£45.00	[ ]
£25.00	[ ]
£32.00	[ ]

14.

£18.00	[ ]
£28.00	[ ]
£20.00	[ ]
£12.50	[ ]
£16.00	[ ]

15.

Kite	[ ]
Square	[ ]
Octagon	[ ]
Hexagon	[ ]
Cuboid	[ ]

16.

(2.6) (1,7)	[ ]
(2,6) (5,7)	[ ]
(6,2) (1,7)	[ ]
(5,2) (1,8)	[ ]
(6,2) (7,1)	[ ]

17.

Kite	[ ]
Parallelogram	[ ]
Rhombus	[ ]
Trapezium	[ ]
Rectangle	[ ]

18

A	[ ]
B	[ ]
C	[ ]
D	[ ]
E	[ ]

19.

1/2	[ ]
4/12	[ ]
3/12	[ ]
1/6	[ ]
1/4	[ ]

20.

8	[ ]
6	[ ]
5	[ ]
9	[ ]
7	[ ]

21.

5/16	[ ]
5/6	[ ]
5/8	[ ]
15/32	[ ]
2/3	[ ]

22.

250G	[ ]
2000g	[ ]
500g	[ ]
1000g	[ ]
1500g	[ ]

23.

24 cm²	[ ]
54 cm²	[ ]
60 cm²	[ ]
48 cm²	[ ]
36 cm²	[ ]

24.

(7,2)	[ ]
(2,7)	[ ]
(9,7)	[ ]
(9,9)	[ ]
(7,9)	[ ]

25.

18	[ ]
16	[ ]
24	[ ]
20	[ ]
22	[ ]

26.

231	[ ]
321	[ ]
239	[ ]
229	[ ]
319	[ ]

27.

12	[ ]
14	[ ]
13	[ ]
17	[ ]
16	[ ]

28.

40	[ ]
35	[ ]
50	[ ]
30	[ ]
45	[ ]

29.

£ 32.25	[ ]
£ 30.75	[ ]
£ 31.75	[ ]
£ 30.25	[ ]
£ 29.75	[ ]

30.

96	[ ]
156	[ ]
30	[ ]
36	[ ]
72	[ ]